ADVANTAGE Reading

Table of Contents

Table of Contents

Be a Sport!

That's Entertainment!

CREDITS

Concept Development: Kent Publishing Services, Inc.

Written by: Linda Barr

Design: Moonhee Pak

Production: Signature Design Group, Inc.

Illustrators: John Keely

Art Director: Tom Cochrane

Project Director: Carolea Williams

© 2005 Creative Teaching Press, Inc., Huntington Beach, CA 92649
Reproduction of activities in any manner for use in the classroom and not for commercial sale is permissible.
Reproduction of these materials for an entire school or for a school system is strictly prohibited.

Introduction

The Advantage Reading Series for grades 3–8 is shaped and influenced by current research findings in literacy instruction grounded in the federally mandated *No Child Left Behind* Act. It includes the following key skill strands:
- phonics/structural word analysis
- vocabulary development
- reading fluency
- reading comprehension

This series offers strong skill instruction along with motivational features in an easy-to-use format.

Take a look at all the advantages this reading series offers . . .

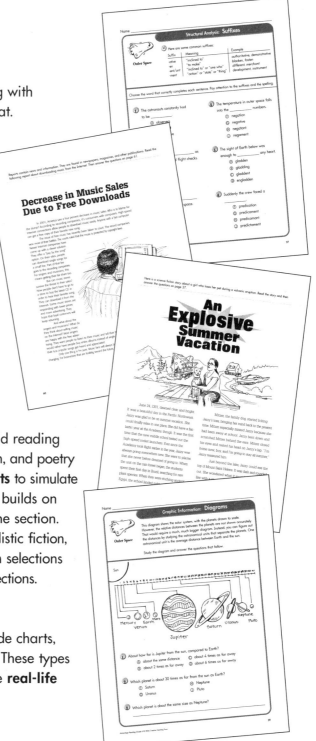

Phonics/Structural Word Analysis
Word analysis activities include the study of word syllabication, prefixes, suffixes, synonyms, antonyms, word roots, similes, metaphors, idioms, adjectives, adverbs, and much more. Word analysis helps students increase their **vocabulary, word-recognition skills,** and **spelling skills.**

Variety of Reading Genres
Fiction and Nonfiction
Students will have many opportunities to build reading skills by reading a variety of fiction, nonfiction, and poetry selections created in a **variety of visual formats** to simulate authentic reading styles. Each story selection builds on content vocabulary and skills introduced in the section. Fiction selections include fantasy, legends, realistic fiction, first-person narratives, and poetry. Nonfiction selections include biographies, how-to's, reports, and directions.

Graphic Information
Graphic information reading selections include charts, graphs, labels, maps, diagrams, and recipes. These types of reading opportunities help students hone **real-life reading skills.**

Comprehension Strategies

Strategic comprehension activities encourage students to make connections, ask questions, make predictions, and think about strategies they can use to **increase their understanding** of the text's meaning.

Fluency Practice

Reading fluency is the ability to **read with expression,** intonation, and a natural flow that sounds like talking. Fluency is essential for comprehension because the lack of it results in choppy, robotic reading that stands in the way of making sense out of a phrase or sentence.

Writing

Reading and writing are partner skills.

A **range of writing activities** helps students improve their ability to write as well as learn about different forms of writing, such as signs, notes, personal narratives, riddles, poems, stories, descriptions, journals, and friendly letters.

Extensions and Real-Life Applications

Each unit ends with a "More Things to Do" page that includes suggestions for **hands-on experiences** that extend the theme. A list of books is also included for further study and enjoyment of the unit's theme.

Answer Key

Answers for each page are provided at the back of the book to make **checking answers quick and easy.**

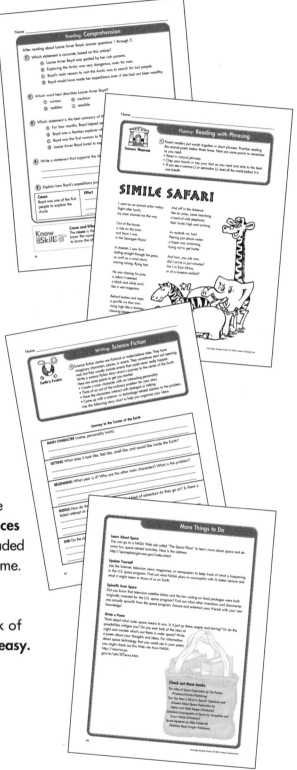

Name _____

Survival!

Comprehension: **Prior Knowledge**

We usually do not dwell on our survival—until something happens to remind us of how fragile we are. Our survival can be threatened in so many ways, by natural and unnatural forces, some under our control and some not. The survival of other animals, both the ones we take care of and the wild ones, along with the plants that sustain us, can be just as fragile.

Think about the words and images that came to your mind when you read the title of this theme: *Survival!* Then, complete the word web below.

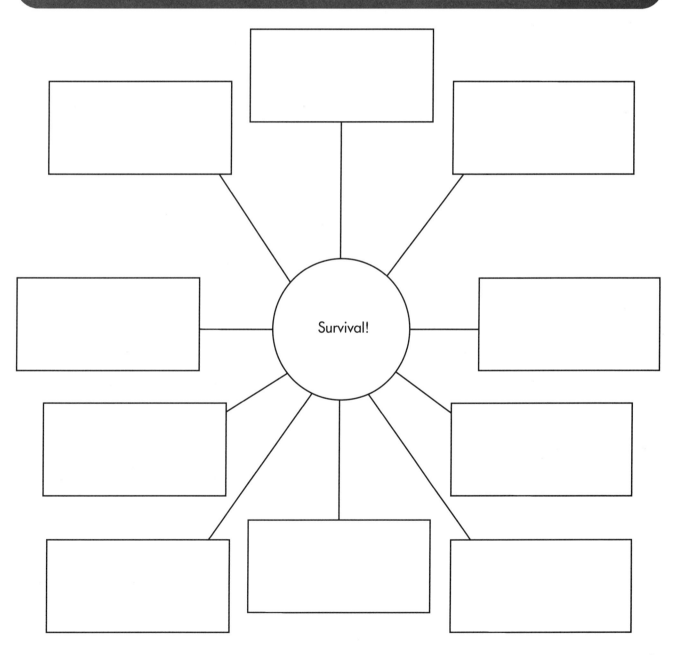

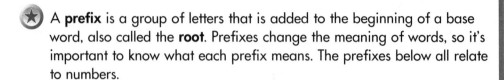

Structural Analysis: Prefixes

Survival!

⭐ A **prefix** is a group of letters that is added to the beginning of a base word, also called the **root**. Prefixes change the meaning of words, so it's important to know what each prefix means. The prefixes below all relate to numbers.

Prefix	Meaning	Examples
uni-	one	unicorn, unity
bi-	two	bicycle, binocular
tri-	three	tricycle, triplet
quadr-	four	quadrangle, quadrillion
deci-	ten	decimal, decimate
cent-	hundred	century, centimeter

Choose the word that completes each sentence correctly. Pay attention to the prefixes.

1 The town is celebrating its 100th birthday, or its _____.
- Ⓐ bicentennial
- Ⓑ anniversary
- Ⓒ centennial
- Ⓓ decennial

2 He competed in all ten events of the _____.
- Ⓕ triathlon
- Ⓖ decathlon
- Ⓗ diphthong
- Ⓙ pentathlon

3 A _____ tooth has two points for chewing.
- Ⓐ molar
- Ⓑ canine
- Ⓒ incisor
- Ⓓ bicuspid

4 The police divided the area into four _____.
- Ⓕ quintuplets
- Ⓖ quadrants
- Ⓗ triangles
- Ⓙ quintets

5 Everyone on the team wore the same _____.
- Ⓐ unicycle
- Ⓑ uniform
- Ⓒ unison
- Ⓓ universe

6 Kevin, Joy, and Sharon sang together as a _____.
- Ⓕ triangle
- Ⓖ quartet
- Ⓗ duet
- Ⓙ trio

Advantage Reading Grade 7 © 2005 Creative Teaching Press

Structural Analysis: Transitional Words

Survival!

Transitional words show how your ideas fit together, making your writing easier to understand. In the example below, the transitional word *however* signals that the next idea will contradict the first sentence.

She planned to be on time. <u>However</u>, rush-hour traffic made her late.

Look at the categories of transitional words in the box. Choose the transitional word or phrase that belongs on each blank line in the questions. Think carefully about how the ideas are related. In some cases, more than one transitional word or phrase could be used.

Time:	first, later, then, next
Contrast:	however, but, nevertheless
Addition:	also, too, in addition
Explanation:	because, for example, in fact

1 I have to finish my book report tonight _____ it's due tomorrow.

2 First, choose a topic that interests you. _____ begin to gather information from library sources or reliable Web sites.

3 He didn't have enough money to buy a new car. _____ , he had no time to search for the best buy.

4 Our school had held the ceremony on the same day for five years. _____ , this year it had to be postponed.

5 The coach really cares about the players on the team. _____ , he makes a point of meeting all their families.

6 Choosing a sport to play can be challenging. _____ , you must evaluate your own skills. Then, you must decide which sport uses your strongest skills.

7 Our science fair project was quite imaginative. _____ , it received only an honorable mention.

8 Take a good book on your trip. _____ , you might want to pack a snack.

Survival!

Fluency: **Reading with Expression**

⭐ Below is an interview with young people who survived the Northridge, California, earthquake in 1994. Practice reading the interview at least three times. Change your voice for each person in the interview. Then perform the interview for your friends and family. Remember to:
- Pronounce all words clearly.
- Vary the tone, pace, and volume of your speaking. Use pauses or a louder or softer voice to stress key words and phrases.
- Use gestures wherever they are appropriate.

Earthquake!

Narrator: The date was January 17, 1994. It all began at 4:30 A.M., an hour when nearly everyone was asleep in Northridge, California, just outside Los Angeles. Today I'm talking with three people who were all seventh graders and in the same class at school.

Reader 1: I remember that we had all gone to a movie that evening.

Reader 2: It was my birthday! Going to the movies was a present from my parents.

Reader 3: That's right. The theater was packed, and we had to stand in line forever. I was beat by the time I got home. Then really early in the morning, I heard a loud rumble. At first, I thought it was thunder, but then it sounded more like a train headed straight for me! I was wide-awake in a big hurry! I didn't close my eyes again the rest of the night!

Reader 1: When it woke me up, I thought it was a truck passing by. But then the ground started to shake, and my mom ran in and yanked me out of bed. Our whole family crammed into the hallway outside our bedrooms. It's a good thing, too, because a second later, all the windows in the house exploded. Boy, there was glass everywhere!

Reader 2: I thought I was dreaming at first, but then I realized the rumbling was real! I sat up in bed, which was lucky, because just then all the books and games flew off the shelf above my head and landed on my pillow! Then my dad yelled for everyone to come into the dining room. We all huddled under our dining room table, hugging each other and listening to my dad's portable radio. My mom's best dishes were crashing on the floor all around us.

Narrator: That night 57 people died and 1,500 were seriously injured. Still, it could have been much worse if thousands of people had been stuck in a traffic jam or working in high-rise buildings. The same area had experienced a major earthquake in 1971, so the houses built since then were designed to remain stable in an earthquake. Still, everyone who lived through the earthquake will never forget it!

    Advantage Reading Grade 7 © 2005 Creative Teaching Press

Comprehension: Draw Conclusions

Survival!

⭐ To draw a conclusion, you combine information from your reading with your own knowledge and experience. Then you reach a decision or form an opinion about something in the selection, something the author hinted at but did not state directly.

1 Choose the sentence that draws a correct conclusion.

Ⓐ One student was cut by flying glass when the windows exploded.

Ⓑ None of the students interviewed was badly hurt in the earthquake.

Ⓒ One student was hurt when the books fell off a shelf onto his or her bed.

Ⓓ The students' families were among the 1,500 people injured in the earthquake.

2 You can conclude that these students had not experienced a major earthquake before. What information from the reading supports this conclusion?

_____

_____

3 Choose the sentence that draws a correct conclusion.

Ⓐ Moving to a hallway protected one family from injury.

Ⓑ School earthquake drills protected these three families.

Ⓒ Having a portable radio gave one family something to do.

Ⓓ The families would have been fine if they had stayed in bed.

4 The three students probably knew an earthquake was possible. What information from the reading supports this conclusion?

_____

_____

5 Choose the sentence that draws a correct conclusion.

Ⓐ The truck passing by was in danger from the earthquake.

Ⓑ The loud rumbling noise caused the windows to explode.

Ⓒ The movement of the ground caused the windows to explode.

Ⓓ The train sound was actually a tornado caused by the earthquake.

Name _____

Survival!

⭐ Some words have more than one meaning, but the context will help you determine which meaning is being used. For instance, the word *bat* could be a "flying animal" or a "piece of sports equipment." You can tell which meaning is being used in this example by reading the sentence.

The player tapped the <u>bat</u> against his spikes before he stepped up to the plate.

In this example, a *bat* is a piece of sports equipment.

Read each sentence and think about the meaning of the underlined word. Then select the meaning of the word in that sentence.

1 The <u>date</u> was January 17, 1994.
- Ⓐ a person you go out with
- Ⓑ to go out with someone
- Ⓒ a day on the calendar
- Ⓓ to get old

2 Going to the movies was a <u>present</u> from my parents.
- Ⓕ a gift
- Ⓖ in view
- Ⓗ to offer
- Ⓙ to introduce

3 The theater was packed, and we had to stand in <u>line</u> forever.
- Ⓐ part of a poem
- Ⓑ a long, thin mark
- Ⓒ a brand of clothing
- Ⓓ an arrangement of people or objects

4 I didn't close my eyes again the <u>rest</u> of the night!
- Ⓕ the remainder
- Ⓖ to stay quiet
- Ⓗ to pause
- Ⓙ to place

5 But then the <u>ground</u> started to shake, and my mom ran in and yanked me out of bed.
- Ⓐ cause or reason
- Ⓑ past tense of *grind*
- Ⓒ the surface of Earth
- Ⓓ an area won in battle

6 It's a good thing, too, because a <u>second</u> later, all the windows in the house exploded.
- Ⓕ to support
- Ⓖ part of a minute
- Ⓗ next after the first
- Ⓙ a product with a flaw in it

Vocabulary: Frequently Misused Words

Survival!

⭐ Some pairs of words are easily confused. They may be spelled nearly alike and pronounced the same or nearly the same, but their meanings are quite different. To decide which word in a pair is correct, you must think about the meaning of the sentence and of each word.

Read each sentence below and think about the meanings of the two words in parentheses. Then, underline the correct word for that sentence.

1 They were all going to the game (except/accept) Jennifer and Susan.

2 I couldn't believe they would (desert/dessert) me when I needed them most.

3 How much (farther/further) is the village?

4 Her shrug (implied/inferred) that she was not concerned about it.

5 The (elusive/illusive) dog managed to disappear into the park.

6 The teacher was (adept/adapt/adopt) at keeping our attention.

7 The managers debated the (morality/mortality) of firing staff who were about to retire.

8 Just before the deadline, the union decided to (except/accept) the new contract.

9 He was so late that I had to (imply/infer) that he was not coming.

10 When you start a new school, you must (adept/adapt/adopt) to the rules there.

11 The gathering broke up soon after the (desert/dessert) was served.

12 The farmer decided to (adept/adapt/adopt) the lost dog.

13 What was the (morality/mortality) rate for this year's flu season?

14 The (farther/further) he researched the issue, the more troubled he became.

15 Her smile was (elusive/illusive), as she had no intention of cooperating.

Name _____

Vocabulary: Content Words

Survival!

How many terms do you know that relate to the survival of plants and animals? Here's your opportunity to find out—and to expand your vocabulary. Fill in the bubble beside the correct answer for questions 1 through 8. If you aren't sure of an answer, look it up in a science textbook or an encyclopedia.

1 Which word means "a place where an organism lives that meets all of its needs"?

- Ⓐ home
- Ⓑ habitat
- Ⓒ biosphere
- Ⓓ ecosystem

2 What is the term for all the organisms in an ecosystem?

- Ⓕ invertebrates
- Ⓖ vertebrates
- Ⓗ population
- Ⓙ species

3 Which term means "anything that restricts the number of individuals in a population"?

- Ⓐ food web
- Ⓑ symbiosis
- Ⓒ food chain
- Ⓓ limiting factor

4 What is the "carrying capacity" for an ecosystem?

- Ⓕ the largest number of one species that the ecosystem can support
- Ⓖ the total number of populations living in an ecosystem
- Ⓗ the size of a population at any time
- Ⓙ the link between predator and prey

5 Which term describes a species that could soon disappear?

- Ⓐ extinct
- Ⓑ diverse
- Ⓒ threatened
- Ⓓ endangered

6 Which term describes gradual changes in the type of species that live in an area?

- Ⓕ biome
- Ⓖ pioneer
- Ⓗ succession
- Ⓙ climax communities

7 Which of these is an abiotic factor in an environment?

- Ⓐ water
- Ⓑ plants
- Ⓒ insects
- Ⓓ predators

8 Which cycle depends on evaporation?

- Ⓕ water
- Ⓖ carbon
- Ⓗ energy
- Ⓙ nitrogen

Advantage Reading Grade 7 © 2005 Creative Teaching Press

This article describes how certain animals survive in the harsh environment of the desert. Read the article, and then answer the questions on page 14.

Surviving in the Desert

To survive in the desert, animals face two huge obstacles: too little water and too much heat. They use a range of adaptations to cope with these "too" problems. For example, some birds simply migrate to cooler areas during the hottest part of the summer. Others, such as the desert toad, hibernate deep underground when the surface sand is too hot for them. Some birds and reptiles are active mostly during the dawn and sunset periods and spend the scorching hours in (relatively) cooler, shady spots. Kangaroo rats live in dens underground and seal off the entrances during the day to keep the heat out. Other desert creatures are completely nocturnal, sleeping all day and staying active only during the night.

Some animals have developed unusual ways to cool off. Jackrabbits, for example, have huge ears with a network of blood vessels near the surface of their skin. The vessels release excess heat from the rabbit's body into the air. Few people would want to take the black vulture's approach to cooling off. This bird lets urine run down its legs, which cools the vulture's legs as it evaporates. Then the cooled blood is circulated back through the bird's body.

The desert's residents have also adapted to the limited supply of water. Some obtain all the water they need from their food. Many excrete very little water in their urine. Some are able to recapture the moisture in the air they exhale. Kangaroo rats are able to make their own water as they digest dry seeds. These rats will not even drink water when it is available, preferring to make it themselves.

So the next time the weather turns hot, try cooling off with one of these animal adaptations!

Name _____

1 Which statement is the best summary of this article?

    Ⓐ Desert animals face too little water and too much heat.

    Ⓑ Some desert animals come out only during cool periods.

    Ⓒ The kangaroo rat excels at coping with harsh conditions.

    Ⓓ Desert animals have many adaptations to help them survive.

2 Which statement is an accurate conclusion, based on this article?

    Ⓕ Desert animals have more adaptations than any other group of animals.

    Ⓖ Animals that cannot adapt to existing conditions may not survive.

    Ⓗ Animals have more trouble adapting to heat than lack of water.

    Ⓙ People need to learn from these animals' adaptations.

3 Which statement applies the ideas in this reading selection to life in general?

    Ⓐ Desert animals can adapt to a challenging environment.

    Ⓑ Survival often requires adapting to conditions.

    Ⓒ Desert animals are fascinating creatures.

    Ⓓ We must protect desert habitats.

4 Write a sentence or two that explains two ways people adapt to a changing environment. _____

_____

5 Compare and contrast a kangaroo rat and a jackrabbit.

Ways the two are similar	Ways the two are different
_____	_____
_____	_____
_____	_____
_____	_____

Compare and Contrast
To compare two things, list ways they are alike. To contrast two things, look for ways they are different.

Should We Have Zoos?

Lately, some people are questioning whether we should keep animals in zoos. They insist that we're doing this not to protect the animals but to make money from them. After all, more than 90 percent of the mammals in zoos were born there, not captured in the wild. Their only purpose in life is to entertain zoo visitors. Doesn't this mean we are using these animals to meet our own needs?

Not at all! Zoos allow most people their only contact with exotic animals. Most of us cannot travel to Asia, Africa, Australia, and so on to see these animals in their natural habitats. Still, we can marvel at them in realistic settings in zoos. Zoos are also helping to breed and preserve species, such as gorillas and giant pandas, that are rapidly disappearing in the wild. Soon, we may not be able to see these animals even if we could travel around the world.

The animals in zoos represent a wide range of species. Zoos help us learn about these creatures and motivate us to protect them. The 213 zoos approved by the American Zoo and Aquarium Association (AZA) must meet high standards in their displays. These standards ensure that the animals are treated well. In fact, animals often live longer in zoos than they do in the wild.

The AZA zoos also support more than 1,400 projects and programs in more than 80 countries. These programs help restore habitat, reduce the hunting of exotic animals, and rehabilitate injured ones. Thus, zoos help animals survive in the wild, too.

Zoos encourage us to learn about wildlife, while protecting the animals in their care. They help preserve species and even lengthen animals' lives. Zoos serve important functions. They should receive our whole-hearted support.

Maddie Randall
San Antonio

Reading: **Comprehension**

After reading the editorial about zoos, answer questions 1 through 5.

1 What is the writer's strongest argument in favor of zoos?

    Ⓐ Zoos help us learn about exotic animals.

    Ⓑ The best zoos are approved by the AZA.

    Ⓒ Animals live longer in zoos.

    Ⓓ Zoos treat animals well.

2 Which sentence makes a reasonable prediction?

    Ⓕ Zoos will grow in importance as a source of information about animals.

    Ⓖ Zoos will help repopulate wild areas with endangered animals.

    Ⓗ To stop the caging of animals, zoos will gradually be closed.

    Ⓙ Every city will have its own zoo.

3 Which statement describes Ms. Randall's viewpoint?

    Ⓐ Zoos have many more benefits than drawbacks.

    Ⓑ The animals in zoos would be better off in the wild.

    Ⓒ Zoos' main purpose is to protect endangered species.

    Ⓓ Zoos are a necessary evil to allow people to see exotic animals.

4 Write one fact and one opinion about zoos.

_____

_____

5 Explain how zoos affect the survival of endangered species.

Cause		Effect
_____	→	_____
_____		_____
_____		_____

Cause and Effect
A **cause** is an action or a problem, while an **effect** is the result of the action or problem. To determine a cause, ask, "What happened?" or "What is the problem?" To identify an effect, ask, "What is the result of this action or problem?"

A fable is a very short story, often with animal characters. It ends with a lesson or moral to guide readers in their lives. Read the fable and answer the questions on page 18.

The Mountains in Labor
by Aesop

One day the countrymen noticed that the mountains were in labor; smoke came out of their summits, the earth was quaking at their feet, trees were crashing, and huge rocks were tumbling.

They felt sure that something horrible was going to happen. They all gathered together in one place to see what terrible thing this could be. They waited and they waited, but nothing came.

At last, there was another violent earthquake, and a huge gap appeared in the side of the mountains. They all fell down upon their knees and waited.

Then, a teeny, tiny mouse poked its little head and bristles out of the gap and came running down towards them, and ever after they used to say:

"Much outcry, little outcome."

Name _____

Reading: **Comprehension**

After reading the selection *The Mountains in Labor*, answer questions 1 through 5.

1 How would the moral of this fable prepare people to deal with real "mountains in labor"?

    Ⓐ They would ignore warnings of an approaching crisis.

    Ⓑ They would be ready to deal with an erupting volcano.

    Ⓒ They would understand the cause of a volcanic eruption.

    Ⓓ They would worry if the mountains went back into "labor."

2 How is this fable different from other fables you know such such as *The Tortoise and the Hare* and *The Boy Who Cried Wolf*?

_____

_____

3 What mistake do the countrymen make in this fable?

    Ⓐ falling on their knees so close to the mountain

    Ⓑ expecting something terrible to happen

    Ⓒ worrying about nothing

    Ⓓ jumping to conclusions

4 You know that "mountains in labor" sometimes erupt as volcanoes or are part of a major earthquake. Write a new moral for this fable that takes this knowledge into account.

_____

_____

5 How does the moral of this story guide us in living our lives?

    Ⓐ It urges us to pay attention to warning signs.

    Ⓑ It warns that a tiny mouse can make a lot of noise.

    Ⓒ It explains that a lot of concern may be for nothing.

    Ⓓ It points out that a rumbling mountain might not explode.

Extend Meaning
Fables offer a lesson you can apply to your own life. That is, you can extend the meaning of the fable beyond what you have read to your daily activities.

Advantage Reading Grade 7 © 2005 Creative Teaching Press

Graphic Information: Maps

Survival!

⭐ Often it's difficult to visualize how an event on the other side of the world might affect you. Maps can help. For example, the Cumbre Vieja volcano is on La Palma, one of the Canary Islands off the coast of West Africa. A volcanic eruption there could send a huge wave traveling in all directions.

If the volcano erupts, the unstable mountain would collapse into the water. Some studies estimate that the initial landslide of 500 billion tons of rock would form a dome of water 93,000 feet high and many miles wide. As the mountain continued to slide underwater, it would cause a huge waved called a *tsunami*. The tsunami would surge across the ocean, traveling north, west, and south at 450 miles per hour. As it quickly reached the Saharan coast, the wave would be 330 feet high. The wave could cross the Atlantic in eight or nine hours. When it reached Florida and the Caribbean, it would still be 160 to 165 feet high. This wave could travel as far as 12 miles inland, causing much damage. Smaller waves would lash the coasts of Portugal and Spain.

Study these maps to see where the Cumbre Vieja volcano is located. Then answer the questions on page 20.

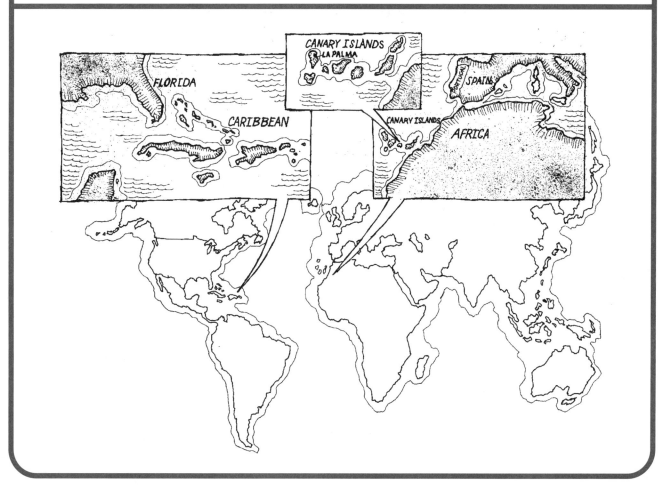

Name _____

Reading: **Comprehension**

Study the maps on page 19 and then answer questions 1 through 5.

1 What effect would the tsunami have on the other Canary Islands?

_____

_____

2 If this volcano erupts, what is the most likely effect on the East Coast of the United States, north of Florida?

    Ⓕ flooding

    Ⓖ tornadoes

    Ⓗ high winds

    Ⓙ a layer of ash

3 Which conclusion is accurate, based on the maps and other information?

    Ⓐ The tsunami would expend nearly all of its energy as it crosses the Atlantic.

    Ⓑ The location of this volcano makes it a threat to many nations.

    Ⓒ The tsunami would also threaten cites on the Gulf of Mexico.

    Ⓓ Coastal nations can protect themselves from a tsunami.

4 Name two or three areas not mentioned on page 19 that are likely to be damaged by this tsunami wave.

_____

_____

5 Which statement is an opinion?

    Ⓐ The Cumbre Vieja volcano is located on the island of La Palma.

    Ⓑ The results of an eruption would have far-reaching effects.

    Ⓒ The people of Cumbre Vieja would be the first victims.

    Ⓓ An eruption of this volcano is not likely.

 **Know THE Skill**

Fact and Opinion
A **fact** can be proved through research, while an **opinion** is someone's idea, based on a belief or feeling. In some of your reading, opinions might appear to be factual, so you must read carefully so you do not accept an opinion as fact.

Advantage Reading Grade 7 © 2005 Creative Teaching Press

Name _____

Survival!

Writing: Fable

⭐ A fable is a short story, usually with animal characters, that teaches a lesson or moral. As you saw in *Mountains in Labor*, some fables are based on natural phenomena. The moral is stated at the end of the story, and all the action leads to it. If the characters are animals, they behave as humans do, talking, interacting, and having the same feelings, conflicts, and motivations as people.

The conflict in a fable should be simple and clear because the story is short. The characters usually solve the conflict in one try—or they might be overcome by it. Because of the story's brevity, the characters are not well developed and may have only one recognizable trait, such as selfishness, ignorance, or impatience. This trait leads to trouble—and the moral of the story.

Write a fable of your own. Remember these points as you write:
• Think of a moral you would like to teach.
• Choose one or two characters, who might be animals.
• Give your characters traits based on your moral.
• Think of situations the characters might face that would prove your moral is correct.

This graphic organizer can help you plan your fable. Remember that the moral will guide your planning, but you will write it at the end of the story. When your fable is complete, think of an interesting title for it.

Moral:
Characters and their traits:
Problem (or natural phenomena):
Solution:

Name _____

Survival!

Writing: Fable

Write the first draft of your fable below, using the notes from your graphic organizer on page 21. Continue your story on another sheet of paper, if needed.

_____

_____

_____

_____

_____

_____

_____

_____

_____

_____

_____

_____

_____

_____

Show your first draft to a friend or family member. Ask this person to explain how you could make your story clearer and more interesting. What should you add, and what should you leave out? Do the characters' actions and comments make sense? Does the story prove that your moral is correct?

Advantage Reading Grade 7 © 2005 Creative Teaching Press

Survival!

Writing: **Fable**

Now write the final draft of your fable, adding illustrations, if you wish.

_____

_____

_____

_____

_____

_____

_____

_____

_____

_____

_____

_____

_____

_____

_____

Disastrous Interviews

Identify someone in your family, school, or neighborhood who survived an earthquake or other natural disaster. Interview this person for your school newspaper. Before your interview, think of questions that will help you learn who, what, where, when, and why the disaster happened. However, do not ask personal or upsetting questions that you would not like someone to ask you. You might record the interview. Afterward, write what you learned from the interview and submit it to your newspaper.

Species Survival

Are there any endangered or threatened animals or plants in your state? You can find out by accessing this Web site: *http://ecos.fws.gov/tess_public/TESSUsmap?status=listed*. This Web site is sponsored by the United States Fish and Wildlife Service and is updated daily. TESS stands for the Threatened and Endangered Species database System. You might study this Web site, choose a species, and learn why it's endangered or threatened with extinction. Perhaps you can join a local organization that helps preserve a species that is struggling to survive in or near your own community.

Zoofari

Visit the nearest zoo in person or by accessing its Web site. Find out whether this zoo belongs to the American Zoo and Aquarium Association and what kinds of programs it sponsors to protect or breed endangered species. Does it ever release animals back into the wild—or has the animals' natural habitat disappeared? What needs does this zoo have, including volunteer opportunities? Share what you learn with others.

Check out these books.

Animal Attractions: Nature on Display in American Zoos by Elizabeth Hanson (Princeton University)
Danger! Volcanoes by Seymour Simon (SeaStar Books)
Earthquake at Dawn by Kristiana Gregory (Gulliver Books)
Where Have All the Pandas Gone? Questions and Answers About Endangered Species by Melvin Berger and Gilda Berger (Scholastic Reference)

Remember the Alamo!

Comprehension: Prior Knowledge

Even if you don't live in Texas, you probably have heard about the Alamo. The defense of this small fort has inspired much admiration and patriotism—along with a few tales that might not be true. What do you know about the Alamo? Who fought there, and what were they fighting for? Who eventually won the battle, and what happened next? What did this battle mean to Texas and to our young nation?

To prepare for reading this section, complete the chart below.

What I Know about the Alamo	
What I Think I Know about the Alamo	
What I'd Like to Find Out	

Structural Analysis: **Suffixes**

**Remember
the Alamo!**

⭐ **Suffixes** are letters added to the ends of words that can change the meaning of the word or its part of speech. A number of suffixes change words to mean "one who." For example, if we add the suffix *-er*, the verb *teach* becomes the noun *teacher*, "one who teaches." Here are several suffixes that mean "one who," along with some examples:

Suffix	Examples	Suffix	Examples
-ar	beggar, liar	*-ant*	assistant, servant
-er	painter, worker	*-ent*	resident, regent
-or	sailor, actor	*-ian*	musician, physician
-ist	biologist, harpist		

Choose the word that correctly completes each sentence. Pay attention to the suffixes and the spelling.

1 It's a fact that every writer needs a good _____.

   Ⓐ editer
   Ⓑ editar
   Ⓒ editor
   Ⓓ edited

2 This series of newspaper articles was written by a well-known _____.

   Ⓕ reportor
   Ⓖ reportar
   Ⓗ reporter
   Ⓙ reporting

3 An _____ must pass a test before gaining citizenship.

   Ⓐ immigrate
   Ⓑ immigrent
   Ⓒ immigrant
   Ⓓ immigration

4 The school _____ is scheduled to attend the meeting.

   Ⓕ superintendent
   Ⓖ superintendant
   Ⓗ superintending
   Ⓙ superintender

5 Our new neighbors are _____.

   Ⓐ Canadas
   Ⓑ Canadans
   Ⓒ Canadians
   Ⓓ Canadiants

6 Automobile drivers must watch out for _____.

   Ⓕ cyclors
   Ⓖ cyclers
   Ⓗ cyclists
   Ⓙ cyclents

Name _____

Structural Analysis: Context Clues

Remember the Alamo!

⭐ If you encounter an unfamiliar word, **context clues** in the sentence or paragraph can help you figure out its meaning. The context clue might be a synonym or an antonym for the unfamiliar word, or the sentence might offer an example of the word or tell what the word does. To identify context clues, look for words like these: *such as*, *for example*, *consists of*, *like*, or *unlike*.

Find the underlined word in each sentence below. Then use context clues to figure out its meaning. To determine whether your choice is correct, substitute the word you chose for the underlined word and see if the sentence makes sense.

1 She was so <u>gregarious</u> that she seldom had trouble making friends.

   Ⓐ shy

   Ⓑ athletic

   Ⓒ immature

   Ⓓ outgoing

2 Fortunately for the suspect, the shopkeeper <u>corroborated</u> his alibi.

   Ⓕ contradicted

   Ⓖ cooperated

   Ⓗ confirmed

   Ⓙ denied

3 He hated to be called by his <u>sobriquet</u>, Shorty.

   Ⓐ mother

   Ⓑ teacher

   Ⓒ nickname

   Ⓓ first name

4 The children were dressed <u>immaculately</u> in spotless uniforms.

   Ⓕ cleanly

   Ⓖ quickly

   Ⓗ immediately

   Ⓙ appropriately

5 The invitation arrived at the last minute, so I was <u>disinclined</u> to accept it.

   Ⓐ slow

   Ⓑ quick

   Ⓒ forced

   Ⓓ unwilling

6 I know it's <u>conventional</u> to eat lunch at noon, but I prefer to eat later.

   Ⓕ time

   Ⓖ scheduled

   Ⓗ traditional

   Ⓙ like a meeting

Remember the Alamo!

Fluency: **Reading with Expression**

★ In 1836, Colonel William Travis commanded about 150 American troops in the Alamo. They were determined to defend the Alamo from the Mexican General Santa Anna and his army. As the number of Santa Anna's troops swelled, Colonel Travis became desperate for reinforcements. He wrote the appeal below. It was carried by horseback to cities around the new nation and printed in many newspapers. Unfortunately, only 32 men responded to this appeal. The Alamo defenders held off Santa Anna's army for nearly two weeks, but in the end all the defenders were killed.

Read the appeal aloud, using your voice to show Colonel Travis' patriotism and determination. Choose important points to emphasize with a louder voice or a slower reading rate. Practice reading the appeal at least three times. Then read it aloud, with feeling, to a member of your family.

**To the People of Texas and All Americans in the World—
Fellow Citizens & Compatriots:**

I am besieged by a thousand or more of the Mexicans under Santa Anna. I have sustained a continual bombardment and cannonade for 24 hours and have not lost a man. The enemy has demanded a surrender at discretion, otherwise the garrison are to be put to the sword if the fort is taken. I have answered the demand with a cannon shot, and our flag still waves proudly from the walls. I shall never surrender nor retreat.

Then, I call on you in the name of Liberty, of patriotism, and of everything dear to the American character, to come to our aid with all dispatch. The enemy is receiving reinforcements daily and will no doubt increase to three or four thousand in four or five days. If this call is neglected, I am determined to sustain myself as long as possible and die like a soldier who never forgets what is due to his own honor and that of his country.

Victory or Death,
William Barret Travis
Lt. Col. Comdt.

Advantage Reading Grade 7 © 2005 Creative Teaching Press

Comprehension: Cause and Effect

Remember the Alamo!

Something that makes an event happen is a **cause**, while the result of an action is an **effect**. Often an effect becomes the cause of another effect, resulting in a chain of related events. Being able to identify causes and effects helps you understand the **sequence**, or order of events, in what you read.

This graphic organizer can help you visualize this relationship. Remember that one event may have several causes, and one action may lead to several effects.

Cause		Effect
_____ _____	→	_____ _____

1. Why did Colonel Travis send out this appeal?
   - Ⓐ He had already lost many of his men.
   - Ⓑ He had received only 32 reinforcements so far.
   - Ⓒ The Mexican army greatly outnumbered his men.
   - Ⓓ All but 150 of Travis's soldiers had already been killed.

2. What was the effect of this appeal?
   - Ⓕ Travis received support from all over the nation.
   - Ⓖ A small number of men joined the defenders.
   - Ⓗ The Alamo's defenders were all killed.
   - Ⓙ Santa Anna strengthened his army.

3. According to the appeal, what will happen if the defenders do not surrender?
   - Ⓐ They will all be killed.
   - Ⓑ Colonel Travis will send out another appeal.
   - Ⓒ Santa Anna's army will shoot cannons at the Alamo.
   - Ⓓ The Mexicans will receive many more reinforcements.

4. What will Colonel Travis do if no one responds to his appeal?
   - Ⓕ He will not lose a man.
   - Ⓖ He will surrender "at discretion."
   - Ⓗ He will hold out as long as possible.
   - Ⓙ The enemy will receive reinforcements.

Comprehension: **Author's Viewpoint**

Remember the Alamo!

★ Often you can tell from a selection what its author values—and does not value. An author usually does not explain his or her viewpoint directly. Instead, you must think about and draw conclusions based on what the author emphasizes and the words he or she uses. In fiction, the characters' words and actions often indicate the author's viewpoint.

After reading Colonel Travis's appeal on page 28, answer questions 1 through 5.

1 Which sentence from his appeal shows that Colonel Travis values patriotism?

Ⓐ The enemy has demanded a surrender at discretion....

Ⓑ I am determined to sustain myself as long as possible....

Ⓒ I am besieged by a thousand or more of the Mexicans....

Ⓓ I will die like a soldier who never forgets what is due...to his country.

2 How can you tell that Colonel Travis values being a citizen of the new United States?

_____

_____

3 Which statement describes Colonel Travis's view of his responsibility at the Alamo?

Ⓐ He will answer the enemy's attack with cannon shot.

Ⓑ He will surrender if he doesn't get reinforcements.

Ⓒ He will protect his men as best he can.

Ⓓ He will fight as long as possible.

4 Based on his appeal, what are some things that Colonel Travis does not value?

_____

_____

5 Based on this appeal, which personal quality does Colonel Travis value highly?

Ⓐ courage

Ⓑ intelligence

Ⓒ compassion

Ⓓ devotion to family

Name _____

Vocabulary: Frequently Misused or Misspelled Words

Remember the Alamo!

⭐ Some pairs or groups of words are so similar that they are often confused and used incorrectly. Some word pairs sound nearly alike but have different meanings, while others are pronounced differently but have meanings that are easily confused. You must be familiar with the meanings of the word pairs to determine which one to use.

Read each sentence and think about the meanings of the words in parentheses. Then underline the correct word for that sentence.

1. You can tell from her (accent/ascent/assent) that she is from Texas.

2. The men were (all ready/already) exhausted from the battle.

3. Colonel Travis ordered his troops to (cease/seize) firing.

4. The hopelessness of the situation does not (distract/detract) from the Texans' bravery.

5. By the end of the battle, hundreds lay (deceased/diseased) on the ground.

6. Santa Anna's army used ladders in their (accent/ascent/assent) of the Alamo's walls.

7. The Mexican general tried to (illicit/elicit) a surrender from the defenders.

8. The reinforcements arrived (latter/later) than expected.

9. The soldiers were (all ready/already) for the attack.

10. Travis worried about the civilians in the Alamo, but they did not (distract/detract) him from his goal.

11. Santa Anna's army tried to (cease/seize) the Alamo by force.

12. A few soldiers were (deceased/diseased) and too weak to fight.

13. In the midst of war, it's difficult to determine which actions are (illicit/elicit) and which are not.

14. Did the Colonel give his (accent/ascent/assent) for that plan?

15. Some defenders might have been tempted to surrender in the (latter/later) part of the two-week battle.

Name _____

Vocabulary: Content Words

Remember the Alamo!

Here is an opportunity to test your vocabulary relating to government. Fill in the correct answer for questions 1 through 8. If you aren't sure of an answer, look it up in your social studies textbook or an encyclopedia.

1 Two nations that support each other are called _____.

ⓐ allies

ⓑ alleys

ⓒ nationalism

ⓓ a bureaucracy

2 In which kind of government is power distributed between a central authority and a number of territorial units?

ⓕ city

ⓖ state

ⓗ federal

ⓙ legislature

3 Which word is another name for a democracy?

ⓐ monarchy

ⓑ republic

ⓒ empire

ⓓ colony

4 Which of these is an authorization to act?

ⓕ mandate

ⓖ embargo

ⓗ filibuster

ⓙ balance of power

5 Which word means "to take control of enemy land"?

ⓐ secede

ⓑ occupy

ⓒ surrender

ⓓ persecute

6 Which word means "to approve a plan or treaty"?

ⓕ regulate

ⓖ repeal

ⓗ ratify

ⓙ recall

7 Which word means "a fundamental change in political organization"?

ⓐ petition

ⓑ revolution

ⓒ nomination

ⓓ constitution

8 Which word describes someone who has the authority to act for others?

ⓕ patriot

ⓖ refugee

ⓗ hostage

ⓙ representative

Advantage Reading Grade 7 © 2005 Creative Teaching Press

Remembering the Alamo

The Alamo was not always a national symbol of courage. It was built in 1724 as a mission. Spanish missionaries lived and worked there for 70 years. Then the mission was taken over by the Spanish military. Next came rebels against Spanish rule. Then the Mexican military was based there. During this time, the mission became the cornerstone of the city of San Antonio.

In the 1830s, the Texas Revolution began. Texans and volunteer soldiers from other states fought the Mexican army for control of Texas. The Rebels were helped by the Tejanos, Mexicans who sided with them. At this time, Mexican troops occupied the Alamo. However, in December 1835, after a fierce battle, the rebels took over the mission.

On February 23, 1836, Mexican General Santa Anna arrived at the Alamo. He brought with him 4,000 to 5,000 troops. Santa Anna intended to capture the city of San Antonio. He was determined to restore Mexican rule over this territory. The Alamo stood in his way. Santa Anna had to take it before he could attack San Antonio.

Colonel William B. Travis commanded about 150 troops in the Alamo. Santa Anna sent a soldier to demand that the rebels surrender. In answer, Travis had his men shoot a cannonball at the enemy troops. Still, Travis knew his men were outnumbered. His only hope was reinforcements. On February 24, he sent the appeal you read on page 28.

On March 1, 32 American soldiers fought their way through enemy troops to reach the Alamo. They were not enough.

March 5 was the twelfth day of the attack. The Alamo's walls were crumbling. The defenders were running out of nearly everything. Their only option was to surrender. Still, Santa Anna ordered his men to storm the mission. About 1,800 Mexican soldiers attacked the walls from the north, south, east, and west. The Texans stood their ground, firing back with everything they had. Among them were Jim Bowie, famous knife fighter, and David Crockett, well known as a frontiersman. Crockett had also served as a congressman from Tennessee.

According to one legend, Colonel Travis drew a line on the ground inside the Alamo. He asked anyone who was willing to stay and fight to step over the line. Reportedly, everyone one did except one man.

Colonel Travis was one of the first to die in the final attack. As the Mexicans advanced, his troops had to abandon their positions on the walls. They withdrew to a building called the Long Barracks. The Mexican army pushed forward. After 90 minutes, only about seven defenders were still alive. Santa Anna ordered their execution.

The number of defenders who died at the Alamo is not certain. Estimates range from 189 to 257. Santa Anna did allow some women, children, and slaves to escape. He gave them each $2 and a blanket. The Mexican army lost 200 to 600 men.

Although the defenders lost the Alamo, they delayed Santa Anna's advance. They also inspired others to fight the Mexican army. At the Battle of San Jacinto on April 21, 1836, a small army of Texans defeated General Santa Anna's troops. They even captured Santa Anna. As the Texans fought, they cried, "Remember the Alamo!" Three weeks later, the Republic of Texas was established.

Name _____

Reading: Comprehension

After reading the report on pages 33 and 34, answer these questions.

1 Which statement best explains the main idea of this article?

　Ⓐ The Alamo was lost because few reinforcements arrived.

　Ⓑ The Alamo symbolizes sacrifice and determination.

　Ⓒ The defenders at the Alamo fought bravely but lost.

　Ⓓ Many brave men lost their lives at the Alamo.

2 Retell the story of the Battle of the Alamo in your own words.

_____

_____

_____

_____

_____

_____

3 *Colonel Travis* was to the *Alamo* as *General Santa Anna* was to _____.

　Ⓐ San Jacinto　　　　　　　Ⓒ Mexico

　Ⓑ the Alamo　　　　　　　　Ⓓ Texas

4 According to the article, "During this time, the mission became the cornerstone of the city of San Antonio." What does this statement mean?

　Ⓕ Stones from the mission were used to build the city.

　Ⓖ The mission was in one corner of the city.

　Ⓗ The city developed out of the mission.

　Ⓙ The mission controlled San Antonio.

A **metaphor** is a figure of speech, allowing writers to describe something by comparing it with something entirely different. Unlike a simile, a metaphor does not use the words *like* or *as*. For example, "The small boat was a leaf bobbing on the waves" is a metaphor. It compares a boat to a leaf. The image of a leaf bobbing on the waves helps readers picture the small boat.

Reading: **Comprehension**

5 Which statement is accurate, based on this article?

    Ⓐ The Battle of the Alamo began the Texas Revolution.

    Ⓑ To win the battle, Santa Anna had to storm the Alamo.

    Ⓒ Colonel Travis did not see the Alamo fall to Santa Anna.

    Ⓓ Colonel Travis is remembered for his brilliant military strategies.

6 How do you think Texas history would have changed if the Alamo defenders had defeated Santa Anna's army? Explain the reasons for your answer.

_____

_____

_____

7 Choose the statement that is an opinion.

    Ⓐ Colonel Travis is a respected hero.

    Ⓑ Colonel Travis commanded the Alamo defenders.

    Ⓒ Colonel Travis had no choice but to keep fighting.

    Ⓓ Colonel Travis tried to get reinforcements for his troops.

8 Do you think the defenders of the Alamo were foolish for trying to defeat Santa Anna's huge army? Explain the reasons for your answer.

_____

_____

_____

9 Choose the conclusion that can be made based on this article.

    Ⓐ The Battle of the Alamo helped Texas win its independence.

    Ⓑ Colonel Travis could have defeated Santa Anna.

    Ⓒ General Santa Anna was a vicious man.

    Ⓓ The rest of the states abandoned Texas.

Advantage Reading Grade 7 © 2005 Creative Teaching Press

A biography is the story of a person's life, written by someone else.
Read this biography and then answer the questions on page 38.

Davy Crockett

Davy Crockett had a rocky childhood. Born in Tennessee on August 17, 1798, he left—or was sent away from—home several times. He preferred playing hooky instead of attending school and had little formal education.

Davy married in 1806 and had two sons. He joined the militia as a scout at a time when settlers were at war with Native Americans. After his wife became ill and died, he married a widow with two children. They all moved to Tennessee, where Davy entered politics. In time, he was elected as a state representative and then as a representative to the United States Congress. He was both elected and defeated many times during his political career. Still, it was Davy's skill as a sharpshooter, hunter, and teller of tall tales that made him famous. Plays, books, and even comic strips have been written about him. Some stories of his skills and experiences were greatly exaggerated.

After one painful election defeat, Davy decided to leave politics and explore Texas. He did not plan to help fight for Texas independence, but he became a volunteer in the Texas militia. He wanted to help govern the new nation.

However, Davy reached San Antonio on February 20, 1836. He was just three days ahead of General Santa Anna and his army. Davy decided to join forces with Colonel William Travis and defend the Alamo. After all, Davy was a future leader of the free Texas.

Nevertheless, Davy would not live to see his dream come true. He fought bravely but died on March 6, 1836. He was probably one of the survivors who were shot by Santa Anna. Still, his legend lives on in songs, movies, books, and coonskin caps.

Reading: Comprehension

After reading *Davy Crockett*, answer questions 1 through 5.

1 Davy had a rocky childhood. What does this mean?

    Ⓐ His family was poor.

    Ⓑ He had a stressful childhood.

    Ⓒ He had firm ideas and opinions.

    Ⓓ As a child, he lived in the mountains.

2 Davy left—or was sent away from—home several times. Which does this suggest?

    Ⓕ Davy loved to travel.

    Ⓖ Davy was an independent boy.

    Ⓗ Davy often visited his relatives.

    Ⓙ Davy would become a famous scout.

3 Why did Davy go to Texas?

_____

_____

4 Which word does NOT describe Davy Crockett?

    Ⓕ outgoing   Ⓗ confident

    Ⓖ persistent   Ⓙ cautious

5 If Davy had survived the Battle of the Alamo, would he have become an important leader in Texas? Give reasons for your answer.

_____

_____

_____

Predict Outcomes

When you predict an outcome, you consider what you read and what you already know about a topic in order to guess what will happen next. Your predictions should be reasonable and logical. As you obtain new information, you must be ready to adjust your predictions.

Graphic Information: Diagrams

Remember the Alamo!

★ The drawing on top shows the Alamo in 1836, and the map below shows how as it exists now as a park. Study both graphics and then answer the questions on page 40.

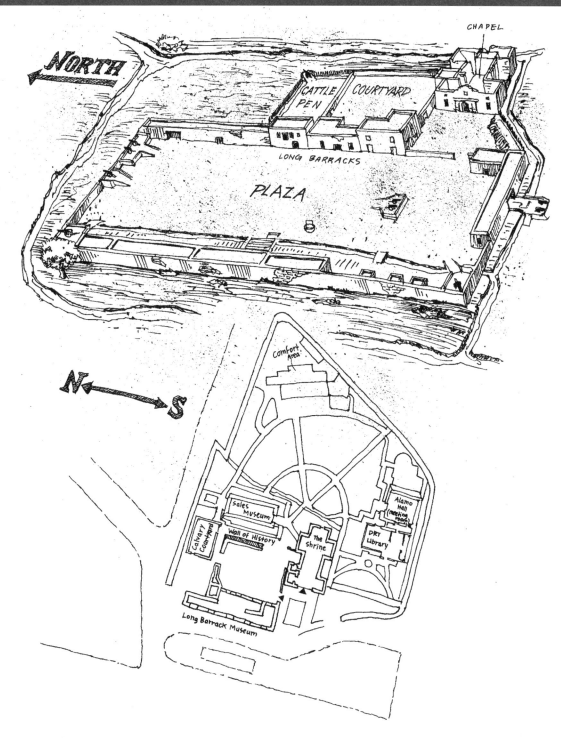

Name _____

Reading: **Comprehension**

After studying the drawing and map on page 39, answer questions 1 through 5.

1 In the park map, which building is on the site of the original chapel?

    Ⓐ Plaza

    Ⓑ The Shrine

    Ⓒ Long Barracks

    Ⓓ Cavalry Courtyard

2 Write two or three sentences comparing and contrasting the drawing and the map.

_____

_____

_____

3 What is the Cavalry Courtyard in the park called in the drawing?

    Ⓐ Plaza

    Ⓑ Cattle Pen

    Ⓒ Courtyard

    Ⓓ Long Barracks

4 What does the diagram of the park tell you about San Antonio's attitude toward the Alamo?

_____

_____

_____

5 Which statement is an opinion?

    Ⓐ The park makes the Alamo look neat and pretty.

    Ⓑ The park helps people learn about Texas history.

    Ⓒ The park retains some parts of the original Alamo.

    Ⓓ Several buildings in the park were added after 1836.

Advantage Reading Grade 7 © 2005 Creative Teaching Press

Writing: **Report**

Remember the Alamo!

★ What interests you about the Alamo? What do you think your friends would like to know more about? For example, several women, children, and slaves survived the attack in 1836. On the Internet and in the library, you can read their accounts of the battle, along with an analysis of how accurate each account is. You can also find eyewitness accounts written by Mexican soldiers who participated in the battle. Jim Bowie, a famous fighter who died at the Alamo, had a controversial role. Just how brave was he? Your research can answer that question.

Here's your opportunity to choose a topic related to the Alamo, learn more about it, and share your findings with others. After you choose a topic and do research, narrow your topic down to something you can cover in two pages. The graphic organizer below can help you plan your report. Choose two to four main ideas to cover in your report and then locate details to support each idea. Adjust your outline accordingly.

1. Main idea: _____
   A. Detail: _____
   B. Detail: _____
   C. Detail: _____

2. Main idea: _____
   A. Detail: _____
   B. Detail: _____
   C. Detail: _____

3. Main idea: _____
   A. Detail: _____
   B. Detail: _____
   C. Detail: _____

4. Main idea: _____
   A. Detail: _____
   B. Detail: _____
   C. Detail: _____

**Remember
the Alamo!**

Writing: **Report**

⭐ Now write the first draft of your report, using additional paper. Follow the outline you made on page 41. After you explain your main ideas and the details you've gathered, go back and write an introduction that will grab your readers' attention and explain what your report covers. Then write a conclusion for your report, summarizing what we can learn from your topic. Finally, think of an interesting title for your report.

_____

_____

_____

_____

_____

_____

_____

_____

_____

_____

_____

_____

_____

After you finish your first draft, look for ways to make it clearer, more complete, and better organized. Ask a friend or family member to read your report and suggest ways to improve it.

Advantage Reading Grade 7 © 2005 Creative Teaching Press

Name _____

Remember the Alamo!

Writing: Report

★ Now write the final draft of your report, using additional paper if needed. Avoid errors in spelling, punctuation, grammar, and word usage. You might illustrate your report with a photocopy of a picture from a library source, or you might print a photograph or drawing from a Web site.

_____

_____

_____

_____

_____

_____

_____

_____

_____

_____

_____

_____

_____

_____

_____

_____

_____

Learn More

The Internet offers huge amounts of information about the Alamo, but Web site addresses change frequently. With an adult, explore sites that offer, among other things, time lines, biographies of the lesser-known participants in the battle, and a virtual walking tour of the Alamo.

Imagine...

What if you were a child, hiding in the Alamo's chapel during the siege? Use your imagination to picture the scene and then write a short story, poem, or song lyrics about the experience. Make sure your writing is more than just a description of the fighting and includes your feelings about it and your hopes and fears for your own future and that of Texas.

Mexico and the United States

Our nation's relationship with Mexico has changed considerably since the Texas Revolution. Our "battles" are economic and political now. For example, you might find out more about the North American Free Trade Agreement and its effects on Mexico and the United States. You might also research the efforts to prevent people from crossing the border between our nations illegally.

Check out these books.

Battle of the Alamo: You Are There by Bryce Milligan (Texas Monthly Press)

I Remember the Alamo by D. Anne Love (Holiday House)

In the Shadow of the Alamo by Sherry Garland (Harcourt)

A Promise at the Alamo: The Story of a Texas Girl by Dorothy and Thomas Hoobler and Carey-Greenberg Associates (Silver-Burdett Press)

Name _____

Technology and You

Comprehension: Prior Knowledge

Technology has developed at an incredible rate over the last twenty years. It has greatly affected the lives of all of us. How do you feel about all the new technological inventions? To explore your knowledge of and attitudes toward technology, answer questions 1 through 5. There are no right or wrong answers, but this exercise will help you focus on the role—or possible role—of technology in your life.

1 On a scale of 1 (no effect) to 5 (huge effect), how much does technology affect your daily life? Explain your answer.

_____

_____

_____

2 What kinds of technology do you use just about every day?

_____

_____

3 In what ways might your future career (or careers) depend on technology?

_____

_____

4 What new technology would make your life easier, more interesting, or more fun?

_____

_____

_____

5 What kinds of technology do we have that you could do without?

_____

_____

Structural Analysis: Root Words

Technology and You

★ Many English words are based on words from other languages, especially Greek and Latin. These related words share a basic part, called the **root**. If you understand the meaning of root words, you can figure out the meanings of many unfamiliar English words. For example, the Latin root *ques* means "ask or seek." Knowing the meaning of this root will help you figure out that the word *inquest* means "an official inquiry into something."

Look at the roots and their definitions. Then use a word from the box to complete each sentence.

Root	Definition	Root	Definition	Root	Definition	Root	Definition
amb	walk, go	dem	people	greg	gather	mim	same
cam	field	fid	faith	init	beginning	mut	change
cand	shine	gnos	know	kine	movement	pug	fight

prognosis	initiative	kinetic	confidence
pugnacious	immutable	congregate	mimeograph
somnambulate	candid		

1. When people meet in one place, they _____.

2. A person who is easily angered might be described as _____.

3. People who walk in their sleep _____.

4. If you believe in yourself, you have _____.

5. A ball rolling down a slope has _____ energy.

6. If you are always the one to organize a project, you have _____.

7. When doctors predict how you will be affected by an illness, they make a _____.

8. When you let others know your opinions, you are being _____.

9. Something that will last forever is _____.

10. One kind of machine that makes copies is called a _____.

Technology and You

Structural Analysis: **Idioms**

⭐ An **idiom** is a phrase that does not mean exactly what it says. For example, if you hear that a friend is "down in the dumps," you know that she is not at the local landfill. She just feels a little depressed.

Read each idiom and choose the sentence that correctly states its meaning.

1 His smile told me that he had something up his sleeve.
- Ⓐ He had a patch on his arm.
- Ⓑ He was wearing long underwear.
- Ⓒ His arm hurt, but he was being brave.
- Ⓓ He was going to pull a trick on someone.

2 Kim bent over backwards to plan a delicious meal.
- Ⓕ Kim's back was tired from standing in the kitchen.
- Ⓖ Kim did everything she could to plan a good meal.
- Ⓗ Kim was completely worn out from cooking.
- Ⓙ Kim cooked while doing gymnastics.

3 Mr. Hunt is struggling to make ends meet.
- Ⓐ He cut a rope too short.
- Ⓑ He is trying to meet someone.
- Ⓒ He is having trouble paying his bills.
- Ⓓ He is trying to get two friends to meet.

4 Don't jump down my throat!
- Ⓕ Don't be angry with me!
- Ⓖ Don't force me to eat!
- Ⓗ Don't strangle me!
- Ⓙ Don't ignore me!

5 Henry has a green thumb.
- Ⓐ His hands are grass-stained.
- Ⓑ He has a mysterious rash.
- Ⓒ He can grow anything.
- Ⓓ His thumb is moldy.

6 I could barely stand to watch that movie.
- Ⓕ I had to stand up to watch the movie.
- Ⓖ I was so tired I could barely stand.
- Ⓗ I really did not like that movie.
- Ⓙ I really liked that movie.

7 It's a fact that money talks.
- Ⓐ Paying someone gets action.
- Ⓑ Money is the root of all evil.
- Ⓒ Money has its own language.
- Ⓓ If you are rich, people talk to you.

Fluency: **Reading with Expression**

Technology and You

⭐ In 1938, many families spent their evenings gathered around their radio. One radio station made a play out of a novel by H.G. Wells called *War of the Worlds*. The play was presented as a news alert, interrupting another program. Unfortunately, many listeners thought it really was the news. As a reporter "at the scene" described terrifying aliens coming out of a meteor that had hit Earth, listeners panicked.

Practice reading these excerpts at least three times, using your voice to show fear, horror, or dignified concern. Then read it aloud, with feeling, to friends. Ask your audience to imagine that they are listening to the radio and think you are reading a real news alert.

Reporter:

Ladies and gentlemen, this is the most terrifying thing I have ever witnessed. . . . Wait a minute! Someone's crawling. Someone or . . . something. I can see peering out of that black hole two luminous disks . . . are they eyes? It might be a face. It might be . . . good heavens, something's wriggling out of the shadow like a gray snake. Now it's another one, and another one, and another one. They look like tentacles to me. There, I can see the thing's body. It's large as a bear and it glistens like wet leather. But that face, it . . . ladies and gentlemen, it's indescribable. I can hardly force myself to keep looking at it, it's so awful. The eyes are black and gleam like a serpent. The mouth is kind of V-shaped with saliva dripping from its rimless lips that seem to quiver and pulsate.

Then a few minutes later in the broadcast:

A humped shape is rising out of the pit. I can make out a small beam of light against a mirror. What's that? There's a jet of flame springing from the mirror, and it leaps right at the advancing men. It strikes them head on! They're turning into flame! Now the whole field's caught fire. The woods . . . the barns . . . the gas tanks of automobiles . . . it's spreading everywhere. It's coming this way. About twenty yards to my right . . . .

After that, a voice that seems to be the President of the United States:

Citizens of the nation. I shall not try to conceal the gravity of the situation that confronts the country, nor the concern of your government in protecting the lives and property of its people. . . . We must continue the performance of our duties each and every one of us, so that we may confront this destructive adversary with a nation united, courageous, and consecrated to the preservation of human supremacy on this earth.

Advantage Reading Grade 7 © 2005 Creative Teaching Press

Name _____

Technology and You

Comprehension: **Fact and Opinion**

A **fact** is a statement that can be proved, while an **opinion** is a belief that cannot be proved. For example, it is a fact that the sun rises in the east, but it is an opinion that everyone should get up and watch the sun rise. As you read, you must be able to separate facts from opinions and use facts to form your own opinions.

After reading the excerpts from *War of the Worlds*, answer questions 1 through 5.

1 Choose the statement that is a fact.

 Ⓐ The radio station should have made it clearer that it was a play.

 Ⓑ This play was based on a novel by H.G. Wells.

 Ⓒ People were foolish to think the play was real.

 Ⓓ The broadcast was too silly to fool anyone.

2 Choose the statement that is an opinion.

 Ⓕ One actor in the play pretended to be the president.

 Ⓖ Many listeners thought aliens were attacking.

 Ⓗ The play badly frightened those listeners.

 Ⓙ The actors were very skillful.

3 Choose the statement that is a fact.

 Ⓐ This kind of trickery is immoral.

 Ⓑ The listeners were not very smart.

 Ⓒ Listeners who panicked did not know it was a play.

 Ⓓ Someone should try this again and see what happens.

4 Write an opinion about this broadcast.

_____

_____

5 Write a fact about this broadcast.

_____

_____

Comprehension: **Analogies**

Technology and You

⭐ Analogies test your understanding of the relationships between pairs of words. For example:

> *Poodle* is to *dog* as *robin* is to _____.

A poodle is a kind of dog, so the analogy should be completed with a word that tells what a robin is a kind of. A robin is a kind of bird. *Poodle* is to *dog* as *robin* is to *bird*.

After reading the excerpts from War of the Worlds on page 48, answer questions 1 through 6.

1 *Song* is to *sung* as *play* is to _____.

    Ⓐ lyrics   Ⓒ acted

    Ⓑ actors   Ⓓ book

2 *Human* is to *Earth* as *alien* is to _____.

    Ⓕ another galaxy   Ⓗ creature

    Ⓖ space ship   Ⓙ sun

3 *Play* is to *entertainment* as *news cast* is to _____.

    Ⓐ broadcast   Ⓒ persuasion

    Ⓑ television   Ⓓ information

4 *Play* is to *fiction* as *news cast* is to _____.

    Ⓕ opinion   Ⓗ story

    Ⓖ radio   Ⓙ fact

5 In this play, *reporter* is to *fear* as *president* is to _____.

    Ⓐ calm   Ⓒ leader

    Ⓑ horror   Ⓓ citizens

6 In this play, *alien* is to *destruction* as *broadcast* is to _____.

    Ⓕ information   Ⓗ panic

    Ⓖ newscast   Ⓙ play

Technology and You

Vocabulary: Frequently Misused or Misspelled Words

★ Some pairs or groups of words are so similar that the words are often confused and used incorrectly. Some word pairs sound nearly alike but have different meanings, while others are pronounced differently but have meanings that are easily confused. You must be familiar with the meanings of similar words so you can determine which word to use.

Read each sentence and think about the meanings of the words in parentheses. Then underline the correct word for that sentence.

1. Some say those who authorized that broadcast were (depraved/deprived).

2. Many people (disproved/disapproved) of the way the broadcast was handled.

3. The detailed description of the aliens was (incredible/incredulous).

4. Presenting the play as a newscast was (ingenuous/ingenious).

5. Radio helped people develop their (aural/oral) skills.

6. At (least/lest) the broadcast should have warned listeners that the newscast was fictional.

7. Radio listeners were (depraved/deprived) of a visual image.

8. A warning (proceeding/preceding) the broadcast would have prevented the panic that followed it.

9. The landing of the meteor (pretended/portended) great harm.

10. A warning would have prepared listeners (least/lest) they think the invasion was real.

11. The actors in the play certainly had strong (aural/oral) skills.

12. The calm countryside should have (disproved/disapproved) an alien invasion.

13. Many listeners were (ingenuous/ingenious) in believing all they heard.

14. Many listeners believed the invasion was real, but a few were (incredible/incredulous).

Name _____

Technology and You

Vocabulary: **Content Words**

Here is an opportunity to test your vocabulary relating to technology, especially computers. Choose the correct answer for questions 1 through 8. If you aren't sure of an answer, look it up on the Internet or in a recently published encyclopedia.

1 What is a communication system created by linking two or more computers?

- Ⓐ host
- Ⓑ network
- Ⓒ gateway
- Ⓓ database

2 What is software that helps users navigate the World Wide Web?

- Ⓕ modem
- Ⓖ browser
- Ⓗ cyberspace
- Ⓙ spreadsheet

3 What is the process of finding information you saved earlier?

- Ⓐ retrieve
- Ⓑ login
- Ⓒ copy
- Ⓓ edit

4 What is a code that will give you access to a locked system?

- Ⓕ port
- Ⓖ password
- Ⓗ hypertext
- Ⓙ command

5 What is a search term, phrase, or question?

- Ⓐ password
- Ⓑ browser
- Ⓒ query
- Ⓓ router

6 What is a complete unit of related data, such as the name, address, and phone number for one person?

- Ⓕ cell
- Ⓖ field
- Ⓗ record
- Ⓙ spreadsheet

7 What does FTP mean?

- Ⓐ First Time Purchaser
- Ⓑ File Transfer Protocol
- Ⓒ Free Transfer Package
- Ⓓ Fire Transfer Protection

8 What is a word or phrase that is linked to other documents?

- Ⓕ megabyte
- Ⓖ hypertext
- Ⓗ network
- Ⓙ port

Advantage Reading Grade 7 © 2005 Creative Teaching Press

Does Technology Simplify Our Lives?

An electronic alarm clock might start your day. Then you might warm up some oatmeal in the microwave and eat it while you watch television or play a quick video game. If you have time, you might check your e-mail before you leave for school. However, chances are good that you leave your cell phone at home. This device is not welcome at many schools.

After school, you probably will e-mail your thoughts and plans to friends and family from your computer or even your cell phone. Then you might search the Internet for information for your social studies report. Word processing will help you quickly create an outline for the report. You might also take a few minutes to check out the latest CDs and DVDs on the Internet. You certainly will not have to look for stamps or beg a ride to the library or the mall. You don't even have to pick up a phone. Communication is at your fingertips.

Technology affects our lives in many other ways, too. For example, doctors increasingly rely on technology to diagnose and treat our illnesses. Technology developed for the space program, in particular, has changed life on Earth. For instance, research into how air flows over airplane wings helped scientists develop a portable fetal heart monitor. This technology helps doctors in rural areas provide better prenatal care to expectant mothers. The satellites orbiting Earth were first designed to monitor enemy activity. Now hundreds of satellites make our communication easier. They also improve the accuracy of weather forecasts.

Still, does technology really simplify our lives—or make them more complex?

Many from today's older generation were born before television was invented. For them, learning how to use new technology often takes longer—and is much more frustrating—than performing the task the "old way." On the other hand, you and your classmates grew up with computer chips and gigabytes. Mastering new devices and programs tends to be easier for you. No doubt, future generations will feel even more comfortable with technology.

At the same time, some formerly simple devices, such as alarm clocks, are now quite complicated. Programming their digital commands seems much harder than it has to be. And what happens to our lives when computer chips fail and systems crash? It's a disaster!

As we become better at programming devices, we will also begin to question whether maybe the old way is good enough. Granted, medical equipment requires a high degree of electronic programming in order to gather specific information. This is a valuable use of technology. But does a kitchen toaster need digital commands? Can't we just push down a lever?

As far as chips failing and systems crashing, we can only hope for improvement. The advance of technology cannot be stopped or even slowed. Perhaps, though, technicians will learn how to reduce the number and frequency of failures and crashes. The rest of us will be forever grateful, both young and old.

Technology does simplify our lives. The price in frustration is still a little high for some of us, but we have hope for the future.

Reading: Comprehension

After reading the essay on pages 53 and 54, answer questions 1 through 5.

1 What is one way that technology makes our lives more complex?
- Ⓐ We can shop without leaving home.
- Ⓑ We must learn how to program devices.
- Ⓒ We can e-mail friends over the Internet.
- Ⓓ We can gather information using the Web.

2 Based on this essay, what can you tell about the age of the author? Give reasons for your answer.

_____

_____

3 Which statement from the essay is an opinion?
- Ⓐ This is a valuable use of technology.
- Ⓑ Technology affects our lives in other ways, too.
- Ⓒ Doctors increasingly rely on technology to diagnose and treat our illnesses.
- Ⓓ Granted, medical equipment requires a high degree of electronic programming in order to gather specific information.

4 Toward the end of the essay, the author writes, "The price in frustration...." Choose the phrase that explains what this means.
- Ⓕ the cost of repairs
- Ⓖ the cost of training
- Ⓗ the number of failures
- Ⓙ the amount of aggravation

5 Summarize this essay in your own words. Try to keep your summary to two or three sentences.

_____

_____

_____

_____

_____

Summarize

When you summarize a selection, you explain the most important points, usually in the order they happened or were presented.

Science fiction includes stories about the future and trips from the present back to the past, via some kind of new technology. This science fiction story is based on reality—the Space Island Group Project. This organization hopes to build a city in space by 2010. It plans to create the city from fuel tanks that are left over from space shuttle flights. To be called *Geodes*, these tanks, now at the bottom of the ocean, are 154 feet long and 27.5 feet wide. Each one contains about 100,000 cubic feet of space.

After you read the story, answer the questions on pages 58 and 59.

Space Oasis

Michael drizzled the water over his limp tomato plants and the dry, cracked soil surrounding them. The struggling plants, a former science project, had been thriving inside so he decided to plant them outside and see if he could actually grow some tomatoes. The water he was using was precious. Last night his mother had boiled pasta for their dinner and saved the pan of water for him. With so little water left on Earth, no one was permitted to use it on lawns or gardens. To water any outside plants, people had to reuse water so none would be "wasted."

Just then Michael's cell phone vibrated on his belt. He pulled it out, flipped it on, and saw the smiling face of his best friend. Zachary and his family had taken a shuttle up to the Space Oasis about six months ago, but Zack called nearly every day to brag about how terrific life was up there.

"So I see you're still hoarding water down there," Zack said with a grin. "We've got lots of it up here, you know, and if the tanks run low, we just flip a switch and make some more."

Michael tilted his phone up so Zack couldn't see his thirsty plants. "How nice for you, Zachary," he muttered. "Some of us are just old-fashioned, I guess, so we wait for rain. Speaking of rain, when was the last time you jumped in a puddle?"

"Michael, my man, I am way too old for such foolishness now, but do you want to see my new trick?" Zachary asked.

Advantage Reading Grade 7 © 2005 Creative Teaching Press

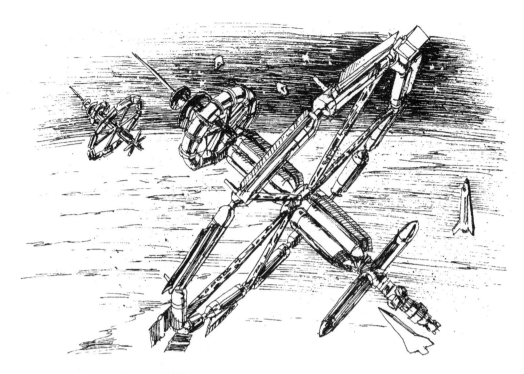

Michael groaned. He had seen enough of Zack doing cannonballs from one wall to the other, among other "tricks." "Zack, anyone could do those tricks in one-third gravity. If you could do them down here, now that would be something!"

"Well, when are you going to come up here and really start living, Michael?" Zachary asked for at least the hundredth time. "You keep saying your family is coming, but you haven't even made reservations on a shuttle. You know how long the wait is. If you don't make reservations pretty soon, I'm going to be an old man when you get here! Do you want to be the last family left on Earth?"

Michael smiled and said, "There are quite a few of us left down here, you know. Those shuttles can only take about a hundred passengers at a time, and there are only 50 of them, so it'll be a while before even the United States is empty. Anyway, are you sure there's enough room for everyone up there?"

"Well, sure, 'cause every flight up here brings another Geode that is already outfitted to become part of a station. We've got six stations up here already, with lots and lots of room for

more." Michael could see Zachary spreading his arms as wide as possible to show how much room was left, all of outer space actually.

"My parents still say we're coming up, Zack, but I can tell that my dad really doesn't want to leave. In fact, he's trying to get a job at one of the factories that outfits the Geodes."

Michael was quiet for a minute, too quiet for Zachary. "I miss you, buddy," he finally whispered.

Michael nodded. "I miss you, too, but if you look out a window up there, you'll see me waving up at you."

"There aren't any windows, Mike. The stations all slowly rotate, you remember, to create some gravity, but too many people were getting sick watching the stars fly by, so they covered the windows. I guess there are still some windows in the zero-gravity section, but I haven't been there yet.

"Some of the people up here are going back…back home, just for a visit, of course," Zachary said softly. "My dad says we might do that sometime."

"I hope so, Zack," Michael told his friend. "Earth misses you, too."

Reading: **Comprehension**

After reading *Space Oasis*, answer questions 1 through 9.

1 Which word describes Michael at the beginning of the story?

    Ⓐ depressed

    Ⓑ desperate

    Ⓒ hopeful

    Ⓓ excited

2 Compare Michael's attitude toward the Space Oasis with Zachary's attitude. Explain how they are different and the same.

_____

_____

_____

_____

_____

3 What is most important about the setting of this story?

    Ⓐ the city where Michael lives

    Ⓑ the year when the story takes place

    Ⓒ the season when the story takes place

    Ⓓ the location of the Space Oasis in its orbit

4 How can you tell whether this story is fiction or nonfiction?

_____

_____

_____

Fiction and Nonfiction
A selection is **fiction** if its events never happened and are completely made up. However, fiction can include facts, such as details about the Civil War, and it can be based on a real event or plan, as this story is. **Nonfiction** is totally factual, such as a report on the plans of the Space Island Group.

          Advantage Reading Grade 7 © 2005 Creative Teaching Press

Name _____

Reading: **Comprehension**

After you read *Surviving in the Desert*, answer questions 1 through 5.

5 Why would looking out the windows in the zero-gravity section not make anyone sick?

    Ⓐ No one lives there.

    Ⓑ There is no gravity.

    Ⓒ You can't see the stars from there.

    Ⓓ This section does not rotate to create gravity.

6 Do you think that Zachary would move back to Earth if he could? Why or why not?

_____

_____

_____

7 Why isn't Michael impressed with Zachary's tricks?

    Ⓐ Michael can do them, too.

    Ⓑ Low gravity makes the tricks easy.

    Ⓒ Michael is tired of Zack's bragging.

    Ⓓ Zack has showed Michael his tricks before.

8 What can you conclude is the major reason why people are moving to Space Oasis?

_____

_____

_____

9 Near the end of the story, why does Zack hesitate to call Earth home?

    Ⓐ He is trying not to think of Earth as home.

    Ⓑ He forgot what he was going to say.

    Ⓒ He is thinking about visiting Earth.

    Ⓓ He lives on the Space Oasis now.

Graphic Information: Charts

★ This chart indicates the increasing number of people who use online resources. Study the chart and answer the questions on page 61.

Technology and You

Percentage of the Population Online

	1995	1998	2000	2005
North America	8.9%	27.6%	47.9%	71.5%
West Europe	2.2%	8.8%	21.7%	50.1%
East Europe	0.1%	1.0%	3.3%	15.2%
Asia-Pacific	0.1%	0.7%	1.7%	4.6%
South/Central America	0.1%	0.5%	2.1%	7.9%
Middle East/Africa	0.0%	0.3%	0.7%	2.4%
Users Worldwide	0.7%	2.5%	5.2%	11.1%

Source: Computer Industry Almanac

Reading: **Comprehension**

After studying the chart on page 60, answer questions 1 through 5.

1 Which region showed the greatest growth in online users from 1995 to 2005?

    Ⓐ Western Europe

    Ⓑ Eastern Europe

    Ⓒ North America

    Ⓓ worldwide

2 Which region has shown the least growth in online users between 1995 and 2005?

    Ⓕ South/Central America

    Ⓖ Middle East/Africa

    Ⓗ Asia-Pacific

    Ⓙ worldwide

3 What are two conclusions you can draw, based on this chart?

_____

_____

_____

_____

4 What prediction can you make about online use in 2020?

_____

_____

_____

_____

5 What pattern of use do you see in all of the last five regions (including Users Worldwide) from 1995 to 2005?

    Ⓐ Asia showed little change from 1995 to 1998.

    Ⓑ They all showed steady growth during this time.

    Ⓒ Users worldwide doubled between 1998 and 2000.

    Ⓓ They all showed a big jump between 2000 and 2005.

Name _____

Technology and You

Writing: Multi-Step Directions

Working with computers and other technology often requires following multi-step directions. Knowing how to write these directions is also a valuable skill. Now you will have an opportunity to strengthen your ability to write directions.

First, think of a process you know how to do that involves at least four steps. For example, can you change a tire, create a flower arrangement, give a dog a bath, install a program on your computer, program a VCR, burn a CD, plant a vegetable garden, or perform another process?

After you choose a process, identify and number the main steps. Then think of the actions that go into each main step and list those, too. The graphic organizer below will help. Add more steps and substeps, as needed.

Step 1: _____

    Substep: _____

    Substep: _____

Step 2: _____

    Substep: _____

    Substep: _____

Step 3: _____

    Substep: _____

    Substep: _____

Step 4: _____

    Substep: _____

    Substep: _____

Step 5: _____

    Substep: _____

    Substep: _____

Advantage Reading Grade 7 © 2005 Creative Teaching Press

Technology and You

Writing: Multi-Step Directions

⭐ Now write the first draft of your directions, using additional paper, if needed. Follow the outline you made on page 62. Begin each step with an active verb, such as *click*, *place*, *fill*, and so on. Number your steps and list them in chronological order. After each step, you might explain what is supposed to happen, such as "A menu will appear."

After you describe the steps, write an introduction that will prepare readers to carry out the steps. Explain when, why, and who should perform the process. List any needed expertise, supplies, or equipment. Finally, think of an informative title for your directions.

_____

_____

_____

_____

_____

_____

_____

_____

_____

_____

After you finish your first draft, look for ways to make it clearer, more complete, and better organized. Ask a friend or family member to read your directions and try to follow them. Then, discuss any confusion that arose and how you might clarify your directions.

Technology and You

Writing: **Multi-Step Directions**

⭐ Now write the final draft of your directions, using additional paper, if necessary. Consider your friend or family member's editing suggestions and avoid errors in spelling, punctuation, grammar, and word usage. You might illustrate your directions with one or more diagrams.

_____

_____

_____

_____

_____

_____

_____

_____

_____

_____

_____

_____

_____

_____

_____

_____

_____

_____

Listen to *War of the Worlds*

To read the entire script of *War of the Worlds* on the Internet, use this sentence as a search phrase: "War of the Worlds Radio Broadcast Causes Panic." At the *About.com* Web site, find "Elsewhere on the Web" and click on "Read the Script." You might work with a friend to act out the whole play, record it, and then play the recording for another class, as if they are listening to the radio. Be sure to tell your audience why this play was so important back in 1938.

Technology and You

Do some research to find interesting new technology to share with your friend. For example, you might investigate new applications of inventions and discoveries from NASA's space program. Amaze each other with possible changes to your lives in the near future.

Space Island Group

You can find out more about this ambitious project by visiting *www.spaceislandgroup.com*. You can learn more details about the construction of this city in space, along with the proposed shuttle fleet to ferry people back and forth. The developers plan to use engineering that is already 95 percent available as a result of NASA's efforts to build the shuttles and the International Space Station. The Space Island Group promises that the city in space will look more like a cruise ship than a space station.

Check out these books.

Computer Technology by Patrice Cassedy (Lucent Books)

The History of the Personal Computer by Josepha Sherman (Franklin Watts)

Information Technology by Pennie Stoyles, Peter Pentland, and David Demant (Smart Apple Media)

Virtual Reality: Simulating and Enhancing the World with Computers by Sean M. Grady (Facts On File)

Comprehension: **Prior Knowledge**

Be a Sport!

Do you like to watch or play sports. Would you like to be a professional athlete? What is your favorite sport? To explore your thoughts and feelings about different kinds of sports, answer questions 1 through 7. There are no right or wrong answers, but this exercise will help you explore your attitude toward sports.

1 Name as many sports as you can. Try to name at least ten different ones.

_____

_____

_____

2 What is your favorite sport to play? To watch?

_____

3 If you could, which sport would you like to play professionally? Explain your choice.

_____

_____

4 Which sport do you think is best at building a player's character? Explain your answer.

_____

_____

5 Which sport do you think is best at building skill in working together on a team? Explain your answer.

_____

_____

6 Which sport do you think best prepares its players to be successful in life? Why?

_____

_____

7 What sport, if any, do you think should be outlawed? Explain your answer.

_____

_____

Advantage Reading Grade 7 © 2005 Creative Teaching Press

Structural Analysis: **Affixes**

Be a Sport!

⭐ An **affix** is a group of words that is added to the beginning (prefix) or the end (suffix) of a word. Affixes can change the meaning of a word and/or its part of speech. Knowing the meanings of affixes can help you determine the meanings of unfamiliar words.

Prefix	Definition	Suffix	Definition
ambi-	both	-al	relating to
bene-	good	-ent	inclined to
circum-	around	-ive	inclined to
hyper-	excessive	-or	one who
magni-	great	-ous	full of
meta-	change	-sis	process or
para-	almost		action
proto-	first		

Look at the lists of prefixes and suffixes and the words in the box. Use this information to choose words to answer questions 1 through 8.

metastasis	circumspect	hypersensitive	paraprofessional
benefactor	ambivalent	magnanimous	prototype

1 When a disease changes position in the body, it undergoes _____.

2 A person who tends to overreact might be described as _____.

3 Someone who helps others is a _____.

4 A person who often has conflicting opinions is _____.

5 A person who is very generous might be described as _____.

6 A person who has some training but not a college degree is a _____.

7 A model for something that will be built or created is called a _____.

8 A person who is cautious and checks around before making a decision is _____.

Structural Analysis: **Multiple Meaning Words**

Be a Sport!

⭐ A number of words have more than one meaning, even though the spelling does not change. You can usually determine which meaning is being used in a certain sentence by reading the rest of the sentence or the rest of the paragraph. For example, if someone buys a yard of ribbon, *yard* means "36 inches," not "a grassy place." The word *ribbon* is the clue to the correct meaning of *yard* in this sentence.

Look for the underlined word in each sentence and choose the option that correctly states its meaning.

1 The men tried to <u>corner</u> the bull in the pasture.
- Ⓐ to trap
- Ⓑ to catch
- Ⓒ a right angle
- Ⓓ the intersection of two streets

2 The dictator ruled his kingdom with power and <u>might</u>.
- Ⓕ a possibility
- Ⓖ permission
- Ⓗ authority
- Ⓙ wisdom

3 The detective tried to <u>track</u> the criminal's movements.
- Ⓐ a trail
- Ⓑ to trace
- Ⓒ a racing course
- Ⓓ a mark left by a car tire

4 We're going to <u>station</u> a guard at each entrance.
- Ⓕ a building for fire trucks
- Ⓖ a store that sells gas
- Ⓗ to assign a position
- Ⓙ a stopping place

5 The senator voted to <u>block</u> the bill.
- Ⓐ to stop progress
- Ⓑ a square piece of wood
- Ⓒ to prevent normal functioning
- Ⓓ to draw the outline of a design

6 The cabin was stocked with <u>staples</u>.
- Ⓕ main crops
- Ⓖ basic supplies
- Ⓗ wire fasteners
- Ⓙ a nation's main products

7 How do you <u>account</u> for this mistake?
- Ⓐ money deposited in a bank
- Ⓑ a description
- Ⓒ to explain
- Ⓓ a record

8 Her letter made an excellent <u>point</u>.
- Ⓕ to identify something in the distance
- Ⓖ to extend in a certain direction
- Ⓗ a statement
- Ⓙ a sharp tip

Advantage Reading Grade 7 © 2005 Creative Teaching Press

Name _____

Be a Sport!

Fluency: Reading with Expression

⭐ Below is a play-by-play broadcast of a girls basketball game. Read both commentators' parts in the broadcast aloud. Use your voice to add excitement and suspense to the game, while still pronouncing the words clearly for your audience. After practicing at least three times, you might record yourselves and then play your "radio broadcast" for friends or family members.

Sherry Pierce   Welcome back, everyone. I'm Sherry Pierce from Student Radio WMND with my colleague, Tonya Finch. I know you are as excited about this game as we are! Let's recap the action so far. This game has really caught fire. The score is 56 to 54. The Central High Lady Explorers are ahead by two points over the Lady Black Tigers of Firestone High. We are in the fourth quarter with 30 seconds remaining in the game. The Tigers have the ball and have called time out to discuss their next play. They're going to have to score on this possession to have any chance of winning this game. Tonya, what do you think the Tigers need to do?

Tonya Finch   Sherry, they have to get the ball inside to Juanita Alvarez. She has dominated the Explorers under the basket with 18 points and 11 rebounds so far in the game. The Explorers have not proved that they can stop Juanita. She clearly is the go-to player for the Tigers.

Sherry Pierce   That may be true, but don't you think the Explorers will be expecting the Tigers to pass the ball to her?

Tonya Finch   You might be right, Sherry, but I know Coach Dean has a lot of faith in Juanita. I think he'll draw up a play to get her the ball down in the paint and hope she can make two points. That way, they can tie the score and then take their chances in overtime.

Sherry Pierce   We'll soon find out. Both teams are coming out onto the court. Shelly Smith will inbound the ball for the Tigers. Juanita is standing to the left at the top of the key.

Here goes. Shelly inbounds the ball to Kelly Davis at the timeline. She is slowly dribbling toward the top of the key, trying to eat away the clock. Latrice Rogers sets a pick for Juanita, who is slanting inside toward the basket. Kelly sees Juanita is free and makes a beautiful bounce pass to her 6 feet from the basket. The Explorers defense reacts quickly and double-teams Juanita.

Can she make the shot with only 5 seconds left in the game? Juanita fakes right and takes a step to her left to face the basket. Wait! She dished the ball out to the wing. Latrice has slipped by her defender and is standing all alone behind the three-point line. She grabs the pass from Juanita, sets, and shoots. It's in the air. It's . . . . gooooooooood! Latrice just sank a three-pointer to win the game!

Tonya Finch   The fans are going wild, and the Tigers are jumping and hugging each other with joy. What a finish! What a great play! Coach Dean sure pulled a fast one on me and everyone else. He didn't go for the tie. He trusted his other players, and they came through for him. Hats off to Coach Dean and his Lady Black Tigers on a most impressive win!

Sherry Pierce   Wow! Congratulations are in order! That was exciting! Folks, I hope you enjoyed our broadcast of the game. Tune in again next Thursday at 7:00 when the Lady Black Tigers take on the Lady Vikings from Garfield High. Until then!

Advantage Reading Grade 7 © 2005 Creative Teaching Press

Comprehension: **Idioms**

Be a Sport!

⭐ An **idiom** is a group of words that does not mean exactly what it says. For example, if you hear that Sam is getting carried away with his science project, you don't expect to see him being lifted out of his chair. You know that he is just excited about his project.

Read each idiom from the play-by-play broadcast on pages 69–70 and choose the sentence that correctly states the meaning.

1 This game has really <u>caught fire</u>.
- Ⓐ The players are hot and angry.
- Ⓑ The teams are playing hard.
- Ⓒ The gymnasium is on fire.
- Ⓓ Someone is smoking.

2 She is slowly dribbling, trying to <u>eat away</u> the clock.
- Ⓕ She is wasting time.
- Ⓖ She is eating a quick snack.
- Ⓗ She is eating under the clock
- Ⓙ She is dribbling under the clock.

3 The fans are <u>going wild</u>.
- Ⓐ They are going to the wilderness.
- Ⓑ They are cheering and yelling.
- Ⓒ They look like wild animals.
- Ⓓ They are no longer tame.

4 She <u>dished the ball</u> out to the wing.
- Ⓕ She threw the ball away.
- Ⓖ She dished out the wings.
- Ⓗ She tossed the ball to a player.
- Ⓙ She had a dish of chicken wings.

5 Coach Dean sure <u>pulled a fast one</u> on me and everyone else.
- Ⓐ He lied to us.
- Ⓑ He did something fast.
- Ⓒ He did something unexpected.
- Ⓓ He ran faster than everyone else.

6 <u>Tune in</u> again next Thursday at 7:00…
- Ⓕ Listen to this station again…
- Ⓖ Listen to this game again…
- Ⓗ Listen to music again…
- Ⓙ Sing a song again....

7 …when the Lady Black Tigers <u>take on</u> the Lady Vikings.
- Ⓐ …when the Tigers take something from the Vikings.
- Ⓑ …when the Tigers take the Vikings someplace.
- Ⓒ …when the Tigers beat the Vikings.
- Ⓓ …when the Tigers play the Vikings.

Vocabulary: Frequently Misused or Misspelled Words

Be a Sport!

Some pairs or groups of words are so similar that the words are often confused and used incorrectly. Some word pairs sound nearly alike but have different meanings, while others are pronounced differently but have meanings that are easily confused. You must be familiar with the meanings of similar words so you can determine which word to use.

Read each sentence and think about the meanings of the words in parentheses. Then underline the correct word for that sentence.

1. The manager questioned the company's (physical/fiscal) policies.

2. During the (finally/finale), the fireworks were incredible.

3. The (message/massage) arrived after she left.

4. The team was determined not to (loose/lose) the championship.

5. He decided to (pursue/peruse) a career as a basketball coach.

6. The stray dog had a (veracious/voracious) appetite.

7. Our tickets gave us (access/excess) to box seats.

8. The outcome of the game was (all together/altogether) unexpected.

9. As part of the (physical/fiscal) examination, the doctor checked his blood pressure.

10. The game was (finally/finale) over after two overtimes.

11. A (message/massage) is welcome after a stressful game.

12. Suddenly, the ball was (loose/lose), so I grabbed it.

13. The players were (all together/altogether) for the team picture.

14. His account seemed (veracious/voracious), but amazing.

15. I (pursued/perused) the program to learn more about the players.

16. The penalties were in (access/excess) of fifteen minutes.

  Advantage Reading Grade 7 © 2005 Creative Teaching Press

Vocabulary: Content Words

Be a Sport!

Do you like to play or watch basketball or baseball? How many of the terms used in these games do you understand? Here is your opportunity to find out. Choose the correct answer for questions 1 through 4, which relate to basketball, and questions 5 through 8, which relate to baseball. If you aren't sure of an answer, ask a knowledgeable person who plays these games or look the term up in an encyclopedia.

Basketball

1 What is a ball that is in play but not in the possession of either team?
- Ⓐ free throw
- Ⓑ loose ball
- Ⓒ bank shot
- Ⓓ blind pass

2 What is the term for contact between players that may result in injury?
- Ⓕ full-court press
- Ⓖ personal foul
- Ⓗ free throw
- Ⓙ rebound

3 Where is the area called "in the paint"?
- Ⓐ in the foul lane
- Ⓑ in the center circle
- Ⓒ outside the foul lane
- Ⓓ between the end lines and sidelines

4 What is a pass from a player who cannot see his or her receiver?
- Ⓕ forward pass
- Ⓖ blocked shot
- Ⓗ blind pass
- Ⓙ bank shot

Baseball

5 What is the term for a base runner pretending to steal a base in order to distract the pitcher?
- Ⓐ bluffing
- Ⓑ delaying
- Ⓒ inside move
- Ⓓ taking a lead

6 What is the term for a base runner advancing to the next base without a ball being hit?
- Ⓕ stealing
- Ⓖ leading
- Ⓗ bluffing
- Ⓙ edging off

7 What is the term for a pitcher coming into a game to take the place of another pitcher?
- Ⓐ relief
- Ⓑ leaning
- Ⓒ pick-off play
- Ⓓ mound support

8 Who are the offensive players?
- Ⓕ the team at bat
- Ⓖ the infield players
- Ⓗ the outfield players
- Ⓙ the team in the field

Can Skateboarders Really Fly?

You may already understand everything there is to know about skateboarding, or maybe you are a beginner, struggling to master the moves. Perhaps you have no desire to get on a skateboard, but you are curious about how skaters manage to control those narrow, slippery boards.

Skateboarding depends on physics. Do you remember Isaac Newton's three laws of motion? They all influence skateboarding, especially the third law: for every action, there is an equal and opposite reaction. Skaters use the laws of motion to soar high into the air—and still land on their boards. This soaring movement is called an Ollie. In the late 1970s, this move was named for Alan "Ollie" Gelfand, a well-known skateboarder. Now it is the foundation for more complex moves.

Skaters ride with one foot in front of the other on the board. At all times, three forces act on a skateboard: the weight of the skater and the force of gravity pushing down—and the force of the ground pushing up. (Remember how Newton's third law works: when you push on a wall, the wall pushes back with a force equal to your force.) When the skater stands still, the forces pushing down and the force pushing up balance each other. When a small push with one foot, the skater can roll smoothly across the ground, but he will not fly into the air.

To perform an Ollie, the skater crouches on the board and then quickly straightens his legs and raises his arms into the air, jumping up. At the same time, the skater pushes down with his back foot, greatly increasing the force on the tail of the board. When the tail hits the ground, the ground pushes back with an equal upward force. As a result, the board bounces up into the air, and the skater becomes airborne.

Then the skater quickly slides his front foot toward the end of the board. The friction between his foot and the board pulls the board higher into the air.

Next, the skater pushes down on the front of the board and bends his back leg, allowing the rear of the board to rise so the board levels out. The skater is at the peak of his jump, just before gravity takes over, pulling him back down to the ground. To absorb the impact of landing, the skater bends his knees.

As skaters perform an Ollie, their feet seem to be glued to the board. However, it's just a matter of pushing in the right directions and keeping your feet where the board is. Skateboards don't really fly, but they come as close as possible!

Reading: Comprehension

After reading the report on pages 74 and 75, answer questions 1 through 5.

1 Which action is an example of Newton's third law?
- Ⓐ The skater pushes down on the tail of the board.
- Ⓑ The ground pushes back against the board.
- Ⓒ The skater crouches on the board.
- Ⓓ The board levels out.

2 Why does pushing down on the back of the board cause the skater to rise up into the air?

_____

_____

3 Which statement is the best summary of this report?
- Ⓐ Skateboarders seem to fly through the air when they do an Ollie.
- Ⓑ Performing an Ollie depends on changing the balance of forces.
- Ⓒ You must know physics to be a skateboarder.
- Ⓓ Three forces act on a skateboard.

4 Why does this report explain how to perform an Ollie?
- Ⓕ Knowing how to do an Ollie allows you to do other moves.
- Ⓖ Readers should understand the physics of skateboarding.
- Ⓗ An Ollie is difficult for most skaters to do.
- Ⓙ The author is an expert skateboarder.

5 Read these steps for performing an Ollie. Then write the letters in the correct sequence or chronological order.
- a. Push down on the front of the board.
- b. Push down on the back of the board.
- c. Crouch on the board.
- d. Jump up.

_____

Know the Skill 👉

Sequence
Sequence refers to the order in which steps should be completed or the actions or events occur in a story or article. Understanding this sequence will help you better understand what you read. Sequence is often related to cause and effect: one event causes the next one.

    Advantage Reading Grade 7 © 2005 Creative Teaching Press

Contemporary fiction refers to stories that are realistic and set in the present time. Read the story and then answer the questions on page 79.

Knowing Your Place

"Oh, man! Do I have to take Whitaker?" Jordan complained, crumpling up the slip of paper and tossing it on the ground.

Once again, Benjamin Whitaker wished he could crawl under a rock. Coach Cunningham made a point of letting everyone who wanted to be on the school football team have a chance to play, at least in the scrimmages, like today. The coach even made it fair by writing the names of all the players on slips and having the team captains for that scrimmage take turns picking the slips out of a bag. Usually the captains just accepted their bad luck when they were stuck with Benjamin, but Ben knew that Jordan really hated to lose, even at scrimmages, and Jordan clearly thought Benjamin wasn't going to help him win.

Still, Benjamin got off the bench and went to stand with the rest of Jordan's team. That was embarrassing too because most of the guys were at least a head taller than he was. Still, Benjamin had seen the movie *Rudy* about a hundred times. If Rudy could be on the Notre Dame football team, couldn't Benjamin at least be a contributing member of the Walnut Springs Middle School football team? Was that asking too much of life?

Benjamin realized he was small to play football, but he was determined. Anyway, he didn't plan to tackle or block the bigger players. He wanted to be a wide receiver and amaze everyone by catching long passes—and then running the length of the field to make the winning touchdown, of course.

Today, though, Jordan gruffly told him he'd be a defensive back. Benjamin guessed Jordan was trying to get him to give up and go home. How in the world was he going to chase down the other players and tackle them?

Regardless, the scrimmage started, and the other team had the ball first. After a quick count, the quarterback stepped back and threw a long pass to one of his wide receivers, who caught it easily, completely ignoring Benjamin's attempts to stop him, and carried the ball for 21 yards before someone else tackled him.

"Way to go, Whitaker," Jordan muttered under his breath as they took their places at the new scrimmage line, much closer to their own goal.

With more help of the same kind from Benjamin, Jordan's team was soon down 21 to 6. On top of everything else, Philip, the school's best kicker, who happened to be on Jordan's team today, twisted his knee early in the game while trying to kick a field goal and had to be carried off the field.

Now it was the end of the fourth quarter, and Jordan's team had the ball. Jordan, captain and quarterback, threw a long pass that a wide receiver named Kevin pulled down. Then Kevin zigzagged down the field, shoving blockers out of the way, all the way to the 25-yard line! With only six seconds to go, the team could still get a field goal—and not lose quite so badly. Benjamin and his teammates grinned and clapped each other on the back—until they remembered that they no longer had a kicker.

As Jordan looked for someone to take Philip's place, his glance fell on Benjamin. "We're going to lose anyway, so you might as well make it official, Whitaker. Go ahead, kick us a field goal."

Benjamin knew Jordan was just trying to embarrass him more in front of the guys, but he took a deep breath and tried to remember how Philip usually approached the ball. Ben waited for Jordan to snap the ball to the holder. As the holder caught it and held it in place, Benjamin ran toward the ball, starting with his left foot. He took four steps, planted his left foot beside the ball, and kicked it as hard and straight as he could with his right foot.

Suddenly, everyone was cheering, even Coach Cunningham. That ball had sailed straight through the uprights, more than 25 yards away!

The rest, as they say, is history. By Friday's game, Philip's knee was still too swollen for him to play, so Benjamin took his place. He nervously missed his first try at a field goal during the second quarter, and his second try at the beginning of the third quarter was too far to the right. Still, late in the fourth quarter, Ben made it, just when it counted most! His team won!

As the Walnut Springs fans cheered, Benjamin was sure he heard someone yelling, "Rudy! Rudy! Rudy!"

Advantage Reading Grade 7 © 2005 Creative Teaching Press

Reading: **Comprehension**

After reading *Knowing Your Place*, answer questions 1 through 5.

1 What does the title of this story mean?
- Ⓐ knowing your school
- Ⓑ knowing what you do best
- Ⓒ knowing who respects you
- Ⓓ knowing where to place the football

2 Do you think Benjamin will become a leader on the football team? Explain your answer.

_____

_____

_____

3 Which event is an important part of the rising action in the story, leading to the climax?
- Ⓐ The kicker injures his knee.
- Ⓑ Jordan says, "Way to go, Whitaker."
- Ⓒ The crowd celebrates Ben's field goal.
- Ⓓ Ben fails to stop the other team's wide receiver.

4 Is winning at football more important to Jordan or to Benjamin? Explain your answer.

_____

_____

_____

5 Which generalization make sense, based on this story?
- Ⓐ All small football players make good kickers.
- Ⓑ Good athletes are always cruel to less-gifted kids.
- Ⓒ It can take a while to figure out what you do well.
- Ⓓ Every school should let all its students play football.

Make Generalizations
When you make a generalization, you gather information, draw a conclusion, and then apply that conclusion to life in general. Next, you must evaluate your generalization to see if it is valid. Does it go too far? Does it make sense? Do you need to add a limiting word, such as *some, many,* or *usually*?

Name _____

Be a Sport!

⭐ If you play a sport, you are accustomed to studying schedules. These two schedules list the games for a boys' soccer team and a girls' soccer team. Study the schedules and answer the questions on page 81.

West Middle School Girls' Soccer Schedule, April

Day	Date	Time	Opponent	Site	Bus
Tues.	4/6	3:30	Blendon	WMS	
Thurs.	4/8	3:30	Kennedy	KMS	Lv. 2:45, Rtn. 5:45
Tues.	4/20	3:30	Kennedy	WMS	
Thurs.	4/22	3:30	Heritage	HMS	Lv. 3, Rtn. 5:45
Tues.	4/27	3:30	Blendon	BMS	Lv. 3, Rtn. 5:45
Thurs.	4/29	3:30	Heritage	WMS	

West Middle School Boys' Soccer Schedule, April

Day	Date	Time	Opponent	Site	Bus
Wed.	4/7	3:30	Kennedy	WMS	
Fri.	4/9	3:30	Green Hills	GHMS	Lv. 3, Rtn. 5:45
Wed.	4/14	3:30	Heritage	WMS	
Fri.	4/16	3:30	Kennedy	KMS	Lv. 2:45, Rtn. 5:45
Wed.	4/21	3:30	Blendon	BMS	Lv. 3, Rtn. 5:45
Fri.	4/23	3:30	Green Hills	WMS	
Wed.	4/28	3:30	Blendon	WMS	
Fri.	4/30	3:30	Heritage	HMS	Lv. 2:45, Rtn. 5:45

Advantage Reading Grade 7 © 2005 Creative Teaching Press

Reading: **Comprehension**

After studying the schedules on page 80, answer questions 1 through 5.

1 Which team will the boys play after their home game at Heritage?

    Ⓐ Blendon

    Ⓑ Kennedy

    Ⓒ Green Hills

    Ⓓ Walnut Springs

2 How can you tell that Kennedy Middle School is farther from West Middle School than the other schools on this schedule?

_____

_____

3 On both schedules, why is the first line under "Bus" blank?

    Ⓐ Those schools are close enough for the teams to walk.

    Ⓑ Those buses aren't scheduled yet.

    Ⓒ The schedules are incomplete.

    Ⓓ Those are both home games.

4 If you wanted to watch the West girls play at Heritage Middle School, when should you go?

    Ⓕ April 8

    Ⓖ April 22

    Ⓗ April 29

    Ⓙ April 30

5 Compare and contrast the girls' schedule and the boys' schedule.

_____

_____

_____

_____

Name _____

Be a Sport!

Writing: **Biography**

⭐ A biography describes all or part of someone's life and is written by another person. Write a biography of another person, perhaps a sports person you admire or a grandparent or an ancestor. You could also write about a neighbor, someone at school, a youth leader you know, or another special person in your community.

The graphic organizer below will help you organize this information. You might change the order in which you present this information in your biography. You might also weave two topics together, such as family history and places the person lived.

Person's name (and possibly relationship to writer)
Birth (and death) dates
Birthplace and early life
Education
Marriage and family history
Places this person lived
Personality
Accomplishments
Other information

Advantage Reading Grade 7 © 2005 Creative Teaching Press

Writing: **Biography**

Be a Sport!

★ After you have gathered information, write the first draft of your biography, using additional paper, if needed. Incorporate information from your organizer on page 82, changing the order of topics, if you wish. Your introduction should interest readers and help explain why you chose to write about this person. End your biography with a conclusion that summarizes this person's accomplishments and contributions and again makes it clear why you wrote about him or her. Don't forget to add an interesting title to your biography.

_____

_____

_____

_____

_____

_____

_____

_____

_____

_____

_____

_____

_____

After you finish your first draft, look for ways to make it clearer, more complete, and better organized. Ask a friend or family member to read it and suggest improvements.

Name _____

Be a Sport!

Writing: **Biography**

Now write the final draft of your biography, using extra sheets of paper, if necessary. Consider your friend or family member's editing suggestions and avoid errors in spelling, punctuation, grammar, and word usage. You might illustrate your biography with a photograph of this person.

_____

_____

_____

_____

_____

_____

_____

_____

_____

_____

_____

_____

_____

_____

_____

_____

_____

Advantage Reading Grade 7 © 2005 Creative Teaching Press

Be a Sport!

Make a list of as many sports as possible. Then choose a new one and try it, perhaps with a partner. Remember, a sport doesn't have to require special skills or above-average strength. Even if you play several sports, there are some you haven't tried. If possible, report back to the class on your experience, explaining whether you like the sport and would recommend it to others.

Spreading Sports

If you really like a sport, find a way to teach it to others. For example, you might volunteer to coach a T-ball team or help with the Special Olympics. You don't have to be an expert in order to teach the basics to someone else. You may learn a great deal about the sport—and yourself!

Good Sportsmanship

With your class or a group of interested classmates, think of ways to improve the sportsmanship at your school. For instance, you might develop a skit and act it out during the morning announcements to help students recognize poor sportsmanship and its effect on others. Or you could create a series of posters for the school hallways or the media center. You probably will think of other ideas, too!

Hold Your Own Olympics

With your classmates, design Olympic events for the classroom. Think of competitions you could hold without disrupting other classes. For example, who can solve a page of ten math problems the fastest? Who will be the first to find a certain fact on the Internet? Use your imagination to think of events.

Check out these books.

Girls Got Game: Sports Stories & Poems edited by Sue Macy (Henry Holt)
Sports Bloopers: All-Star Flubs and Fumbles by Mark Huebner and Brad Wilson (Firefly Books)

Also look for books about your favorite sport or a sport you would like to know more about. You'll have many choices! In addition, you can find biographies of many sports heroes from Willie Mays, to Sonia Henie, to Tiger Woods.

Name _____

That's Entertainment!

Comprehension: **Prior Knowledge**

What words and phrases come to your mind when you hear the word *entertainment*? To get started on this theme, fill in the word web below. You might add words and phrases that range from playing video games to camping. Then on a separate sheet of paper, have a friend or family member complete the same web. Compare webs and then answer the two questions below.

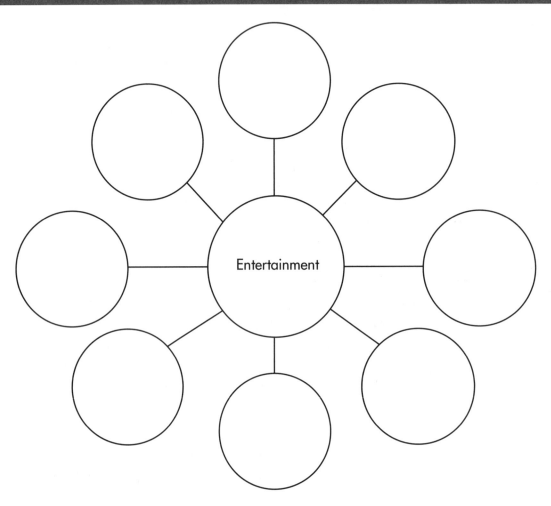

Entertainment

1) How is your web similar to and different from a friend or family member's web?

_____

_____

2) Why are these differences neither right nor wrong?

_____

_____

Advantage Reading Grade 7 © 2005 Creative Teaching Press

Name _____

That's Entertainment!

Structural Analysis: Similes and Metaphors

Writers use similes and metaphors as a colorful way to describe people, objects, ideas, and experiences. A **simile** is a comparison of two unlike things using the words *like* or *as*. For example:

It was as much fun as being caught in a traffic jam.

A **metaphor** also compares two unlike things, but it does not use the words *like* or *as*. This sentence uses a metaphor:

The moon was a white island in the sky.

1 Choose the sentence that best explains this simile:

Her help was as welcome as a wool scarf on a frigid day.

- Ⓐ She needed a scarf on that cold day.
- Ⓑ Her wool scarf kept her warm.
- Ⓒ Her help filled a real need.
- Ⓓ She welcomed everyone.

2 Choose the sentence that best explains this simile:

His story was as smooth as glass.

- Ⓕ I could see through his lies.
- Ⓖ He spoke without hesitating.
- Ⓗ I saw him through a window.
- Ⓙ He told us how glass is made.

3 Choose the sentence that best explains this metaphor:

She was a lion, stalking a good buy.

- Ⓐ She was stalking a lion.
- Ⓑ She was shopping at the mall.
- Ⓒ She was sneaking up on a lion.
- Ⓓ She was quietly searching the store.

4 Choose the sentence that best explains this metaphor:

He was a big fish in a little pond.

- Ⓕ He was important in that small group.
- Ⓖ He could swim like a fish in a pond.
- Ⓗ He was the biggest person there.
- Ⓙ He resembled a fish.

Name _____

That's Entertainment!

⭐ **Analogies** test your understanding of the relationships between pairs of words. For example:

Bread is to *eat* as *milk* is to _____.

You eat bread, so the analogy should be completed with a word that tells what you do with milk. *Bread* is to *eat* as *milk* is to *drink*. Analogies might also involve other relationships, such as pairs of synonyms or antonyms or cause-effect relationships.

Study the analogies below. Figure out how the first pair of words is related, and then choose the correct word to complete the second pair.

1 *Bright* is to *dull* as *near* is to _____.

   Ⓐ blunt
   Ⓑ shiny
   Ⓒ close
   Ⓓ far

2 *Teacher* is to *chalkboard* as *farmer* is to _____.

   Ⓕ farm
   Ⓖ crops
   Ⓗ tractor
   Ⓙ overhead

3 *Neglect* is to *forget* as *permit* is to _____.

   Ⓐ allow
   Ⓑ abuse
   Ⓒ reject
   Ⓓ refuse

4 *Rain* is to *flood* as *polish* is to _____.

   Ⓕ drought
   Ⓖ shine
   Ⓗ shoe
   Ⓙ wax

5 *Eagle* is to *rabbit* as *robin* is to _____.

   Ⓐ hawk
   Ⓑ worm
   Ⓒ mouse
   Ⓓ chipmunk

6 *Education* is to *school* as *information* is to _____.

   Ⓕ knowledge
   Ⓖ learning
   Ⓗ library
   Ⓙ facts

Advantage Reading Grade 7 © 2005 Creative Teaching Press

That's Entertainment!

Fluency: **Reading with Accuracy**

The poem below is fun to read aloud but tricky. The spelling of the words makes us expect to hear ourselves saying other words. Also, the meaning of a sentence might be unclear until you hear the words read aloud. In fact, it is difficult to read this poem aloud smoothly. Read it aloud yourself at least three times, until you can read without hesitating. Then read the poem to friends or family members, but be sure to give your audience a copy of the poem so they will appreciate your task!

A Misspelled Tail

Elizabeth T. Corbett

A little buoy said, "Mother, deer,
   May I go out too play?
The son is bright, the heir is clear,
   Owe, mother, don't say neigh!"
"Go fourth, my sun," the mother said.
   The ant said, "Take ewer slay,
Your gneiss knew sled, awl painted read,
   Butt dew knot lose your weigh."
"Ah, know," he cried, and sought the street
   With hart sew full of glee —
The whether changed — and snow and sleet,
   And reign, fell steadily.
Threw snowdrifts grate, threw watery pool,

He flue with mite and mane —
Said he, "Though I wood walk by rule,
   I am not rite, 'tis plane.
"I'd like to meat sum kindly sole,
   For hear gnu dangers weight,
And yonder stairs a treacherous whole —
   Two sloe has been my gate.
"A peace of bred, a nice hot stake,
   I'd chews if I were home,
This crewel fete my hart will brake,
   Eye love knot thus to roam.
"I'm week and pail, I've mist my rode,"
   But here a carte came past,
He and his sled were safely toad
   Back two his home at last.

That's Entertainment!

Comprehension: Make Inferences

⭐ To make an inference, you first consider what you know and what you have read. Next, you draw a conclusion, forming an opinion about the topic. Then you go one step further and apply your conclusion to a broader topic or to another situation. Last, you check your inference to make sure you did not go too far and assume something that does not make sense.

Read each group of statements and select the option that is a reasonable inference. Notice that some of the statements are facts from the poem on page 89, not inferences. Other statements are incorrect, based on the poem.

1 Choose the statement that makes a reasonable inference.

    Ⓐ The mother warns her son to watch the weather.

    Ⓑ The main character in the poem is a small boy.

    Ⓒ The boy has lost his way before.

    Ⓓ The boy is a poor speller.

2 Choose the statement that makes a reasonable inference.

    Ⓕ The bad weather confuses the boy.

    Ⓖ Getting lost does not bother the boy.

    Ⓗ The boy has to deal with both snow and rain.

    Ⓙ An aunt lives with or is visiting the boy's family.

3 Choose the statement that makes a reasonable inference.

    Ⓐ No one has warned the boy not to talk to strangers.

    Ⓑ A stranger helps the boy get back home.

    Ⓒ The boy does not enjoy his adventure.

    Ⓓ The boy falls into a hole.

4 Choose the statement that makes a reasonable inference.

    Ⓕ The poem is based on the author's experience as a child.

    Ⓖ The poem is based on the author's experience as a mother.

    Ⓗ The author started with a list of words to use in the poem.

    Ⓙ The author started with a list of events to include in the poem.

Advantage Reading Grade 7 © 2005 Creative Teaching Press

Name _____

That's
Entertainment!

Comprehension: Homophones

Homophones are words that sound the same but have different meanings and different spellings. One example is the words *to*, *two*, and *too*. These pairs or groups of words are easily misused, so you need to recognize the variations in spelling and understand what each one means.

Read the sentences below, study the words in parentheses, and underline the correct spelling for each sentence.

1 The captain maneuvered his ship around the (buoys/boys).

2 After dinner, I went outside for some fresh (heir/air).

3 Which planet is the (fourth/forth) from the sun?

4 The senator rose and voted (neigh/nay) on the bill.

5 Which (weigh/way/whey) should we go to get home?

6 Did you hear the (weather/whether) forecast on the news?

7 The jockey held the (rains/reigns/reins) firmly in his hand.

8 To get to the auditorium, go (through/threw) the second door on the right.

9 The hawk (flue/flew/flu) directly over our heads.

10 You have the (right/write/rite) to remain silent.

11 How many (meats/metes/meets) will the track team have?

12 What is the (some/sum) of all your purchases today?

13 I thought I (knew/gnu/new) the answer to that question.

14 Did you read the (hole/whole) book, cover to cover?

15 She cut the pizza and gave us each a (peace/piece).

16 In the afternoon, we (rode/road/rowed) the boat out to the island.

Name _____

That's Entertainment!

Vocabulary: Frequently Misused or Misspelled Words

The English language contains many homophones, pairs or groups of words are sound alike but have different spellings and meanings. You just studied some on page 91, but below are more of them. You must be familiar with the meanings of similar words so you can determine which word to use.

Read each sentence and think about the meanings of the words in parentheses. Then underline the correct homophone for that sentence.

1 The directions say not to (altar/alter) the recipe in any way.

2 The porter gave me some (assistance/assistants) in carrying my bags.

3 The homecoming queen had six (attendance/attendants).

4 The (aisles/isles) in the store were crowded with merchandise.

5 A hospital (aid/aide) pushed me in a wheelchair.

6 The canoe was leaking, so we had to (bale/bail) it out.

7 Our team's loss had no (baring/bearing) on our standing in the polls.

8 What was the (basis/bases) of his argument?

9 Did you see that cereal in an (add/ad) on television?

10 The store finally (billed/build) me for my new jacket.

11 How many (borders/boarders) live in that rooming house?

12 The pirate ship went down with a load of gold (bouillon/bullion).

13 The horse escaped from its (choral/coral/chorale/corral).

14 The owner met us at the building (site/cite/sight).

15 Use only the most (current/currant) information in your report.

16 What kind of (council/counsel) did he give you?

Advantage Reading Grade 7 © 2005 Creative Teaching Press

Name _____

That's Entertainment!

Vocabulary: **Content Words**

Entertainment has a vocabulary of its own. See how many words related to entertainment you understand by choosing the correct answer for questions 1 through 8. If you aren't sure of an answer, ask a knowledgeable person or look the term up in an encyclopedia.

1 Which person plans the movements for a dance?
- Ⓐ choreographer
- Ⓑ conductor
- Ⓒ composer
- Ⓓ vocalist

2 Which person is always an author?
- Ⓕ playwright
- Ⓖ conductor
- Ⓗ exhibitor
- Ⓙ director

3 What is another name for a movie?
- Ⓐ cinema
- Ⓑ gallery
- Ⓒ theater
- Ⓓ exhibition

4 Which of these is a room or building used to display art?
- Ⓕ gallery
- Ⓖ stadium
- Ⓗ footlights
- Ⓙ concert hall

5 What do the letters *DVD* originally stand for?
- Ⓐ digital video disc
- Ⓑ digital versus disc
- Ⓒ digital video display
- Ⓓ dependable value disc

6 What did the term *sitcom* originally mean?
- Ⓕ on-site comedy
- Ⓖ situation comedy
- Ⓗ sit and communicate
- Ⓙ situation commercial

7 Which of these is a factual film about a topic?
- Ⓐ documentary
- Ⓑ broadcast
- Ⓒ cinema
- Ⓓ sitcom

8 In a play, what is another term for the set?
- Ⓕ scenery
- Ⓖ wings
- Ⓗ stage
- Ⓙ pit

Who in the World Thought Up Harry Potter?

Have you read one or all of JK Rowling's Harry Potter books? If so, you certainly are not alone, as more than 250 million of these books have been sold worldwide. The Harry Potter books have been translated into 55 languages, including Latin and ancient Greek. Joanne K. Rowling writes about wizards and magic spells, but before she became a celebrity, her life was more gritty than magical. Rowling (pronounced rolling) was born in 1965 in England, two years before her younger sister, Di. During their childhood, Joanne made up many stories for Di and remembers that they tended to feature talking rabbits. Rowling knew then that she wanted to be a writer, but she didn't tell anyone. She thought others would laugh and say that would never happen.

In school, Rowling was quiet and terrible at sports, as she recalls. She loved languages and English and continued to write stories, but she hid most of them. She did show her friends some of the stories in which they starred, with different names, of course.

At college, Rowling majored in French at her parents' insistence. They wanted her to prepare for a career as a bilingual secretary. However, when she began working as a secretary, the bits of stories that came into Rowling's mind often distracted her from her duties, so she did not excel in that career. At age 26, Rowling gave up on office work and traveled to Portugal to teach English. With her classes in the afternoons and evenings, she could spend her mornings writing.

Soon Rowling had a good start on her third novel, having thrown out the first two. This new book was about a boy who found out that he was a wizard and was sent to wizard school and...well, you probably know what happened next. For the boy's last name, Rowling borrowed the name of a childhood friend, Ian Potter.

During this time, Rowling also married, had a baby girl, and then divorced. She ended up living in Edinburgh, Scotland, with her baby and no job. They lived on public assistance, which is like welfare in the United States. Nevertheless, Rowling did manage to finish her first Harry Potter novel, writing it by hand, as she still does.

It took a year for Rowling to find a publisher for her first novel. Several publishers read her manuscript and turned it down. (Imagine how they feel now!) In 1997, Bloomsbury Publishing bought and printed *Harry Potter and the Sorcerer's Stone*, which immediately became a success. The publisher decided to use Rowling's initials instead of her first and middle names so that readers would not know whether the author was a man or a woman. (They do now!)

This first book was followed by *The Chamber of Secrets* and *The Prisoner of Azkaban*. Fans could not get enough of Harry and the Muggles. Rowling's fourth book, *The Goblet of Fire*, sold three million copies in 48 hours. Fans were just as eager to read her fifth book, *The Order of Phoenix*. Rowling has received many awards and honors for her books, which are now published by Scholastic.

In 2001, Rowling married Dr. Neil Murray, and two years later she had her second child, a boy. The family lives in Scotland now. Rowling still intends to write at least seven books, one for each year that Harry Potter spent at wizard school. Warner Brothers is busy making her books into equally successful movies. The first two grossed $2 billion, and DVD and video sales have brought in another $500 million so far. Of course, you know about all the Harry Potter products that are available, from mugs, to toys, to posters, to clothing, to DVDs.

As a result of all this success, by April 2004 JK Rowling was worth $1 billion dollars. At age 38, she was one of only five self-made billionaire women and the first billionaire author.

And she's still writing! More importantly, many teachers give her credit for creating a whole new generation of readers.

Reading: **Comprehension**

After reading the biography on pages 94 and 95, answer questions 1 through 5.

1 Summarize JK Rowling's life so far in your own words.

_____

_____

_____

_____

_____

2 Rowling has created a new generation of readers. What does this mean?

- Ⓕ She writes books for young people.
- Ⓖ Her books are being made into successful movies.
- Ⓗ Even young people who do not like to read cannot resist the Harry Potter books.
- Ⓙ Many people are interested in reading more about Rowling's life and experiences.

3 What is the most important reason why Rowling continues to write?

- Ⓐ She has signed contracts with her publisher.
- Ⓑ She needs to support her children.
- Ⓒ She loves being rich and famous.
- Ⓓ She loves to write.

4 *Rowling* is to *imagination* as *athlete* is to _____ .

- Ⓕ strength
- Ⓗ writing
- Ⓖ books
- Ⓙ fans

5 Could there be unknown writers who are just as talented as JK Rowling? Explain your answer.

_____

_____

_____

Many myths were created long ago to help people understand natural phenomena, such as the sun "rising" in the east and the seasons changing. Myths were also written to explain the unusual traits of some animals, such as the giraffe's long neck and the leopard's spots. The myth below was written to explain what happened to extinct birds called *dodos*. Read the myth and then answer the questions on pages 100 and 101.

The Dodos' Demise

Long, long ago, millions of years, actually, a group of very special birds came to live on the island of Mauritius. Now Mauritius is a tiny island 500 miles east of Madagascar. Madagascar, in turn, is a large island off the southeast coast of Africa. Both islands are in the Indian Ocean, very far from where you live.

No one knows where these special birds came from. Still, it was soon clear that they were meant to rule the other animals on Mauritius. The birds were quite large, weighing up to 50 pounds each, and always hungry. Yet hunger was never a long-term problem on this island, as plenty of fruit lay under the trees, and plenty of small fish swam in the ponds and rivers.

More importantly for these birds, the island had no large predators. The birds, who called themselves monarchs to describe their position on the island, did not need to beware of lions or alligators or anything else with sharp, pointy teeth. They were free to live in peace and tranquillity. Their wings were rather small for such magnificent birds, but that, too, was not a problem. The monarchs had no need to fly, which, as you can imagine, requires a great deal of energy. Instead, they could spend their energy overseeing the other animals' activities.

For example, a monarch named Christopher the Third had taken it upon himself to monitor a family of rabbits. The ignorant rabbits had been living in dreadful, smelly holes in the ground. However, Christopher had informed them that they would be better off in a home built of small rocks. Nevertheless, as he directed the rabbit family in the construction of their new home, the rocks just would not pile up. They kept slipping and sliding all over the place.

"Hurry up there, you rodents!" commanded Christopher. "If you weren't so slow and lazy, you'd have a nice new home by now!" With that, he gobbled up several of the small stones the rabbits had gathered. The monarchs, you see, had one strange habit. All right, they had more than one, but this one was really unusual. They would eat small stones. They claimed the stones helped ease their digestion, which was not a small matter, considering how much each bird ate every day.

The rabbits, as you can imagine, were not thrilled with Christopher's "guidance." Still, they knew that the monarchs could deliver a wicked bite if annoyed. They also figured that Christopher would soon get hungry and waddle off to find a large snack. So, muttering to themselves, the rabbits kept trying to pile the stones into walls.

In this way and others too numerous to mention, the monarchs devoted their lives to helping the other animals better themselves. In turn, they expected the animals' adoration. Certainly, as they waddled around the island, the other animals cleared the way in honor of their importance. While some of the animals seemed to be snickering behind their paws, the monarchs were not concerned. They always had more significant things to consider, such as the location of their next meal.

In 1598, however, a dramatic change occurred on the peaceful island. A group of tall animals with only two legs appeared on the beach. They had been traveling over the water in a wooden contraption made from trees, it seemed. The monarchs, of course, were the first to investigate these strange animals. After all, they might turn out to be useful in some way.

When the new animals saw the monarchs, they made a strange noise that sounded like, "Ha, ha, ha!" The monarchs had never heard this noise before and guessed it was how the new animals showed their respect. That had to be it.

Then the new animals motioned to one of the monarchs, Charles the Fourth. The other monarchs whispered to each other excitedly, "They are inviting Charles to get on their wooden contraption! They must hope he will approve of it!"

Advantage Reading Grade 7 © 2005 Creative Teaching Press

Sure enough, the new animals made way for Charles to waddle up a board and onto their traveling device. Soon after, the monarchs thought they heard a squawk, but probably not.

The next day, the monarchs did not see Charles, so they guessed that the new animals had invited him to stay on the wooden device overnight. These new animals certainly seemed to have good manners, except for the way they pointed at the monarchs and said, "Doudo! Doudo!" It seemed to be the animals' name for them. The monarchs discussed this development and decided they would accept this new name for themselves, shortening it a bit to *dodo*. That was easier to say than *monarch*, anyway, and far easier to spell. From now on, they would be the dodos.

Over the next months, more of the new animals arrived in larger wooden contraptions. The animals, who were called *sailors*, were always so gracious, inviting a few dodos to visit their ships every day. Of course, those dodos were always so impressed with the sailors' hospitality that they decided to stay and live on the ships.

The rabbits and other animals didn't visit the sailors on their ships, but the dodos knew the sailors couldn't be bothered entertaining such miserable creatures. Late every day, several dodos would gather on the shore and wait for an invitation to come aboard the ships. When the sailors beckoned them, the dodos would smile at those who weren't invited and waddle up onto the ships.

After a while, there weren't many dodos living on Mauritius anymore. They were all living on the ships. Every day, the ones who were left waited anxiously on the shore. "Take me!" they called. "I haven't visited yet!" The sailors probably did not understand the dodos' language, but they were still polite enough to invite them aboard.

One day in 1681, the last dodo was invited on a ship. He turned and smiled proudly at the other animals, who watched from the forest's edge. Perhaps he did not notice that they were grinning.

Name _____

Reading: **Comprehension**

After reading *The Dodos' Demise*, answer questions 1 through 10.

1 What does the word *demise* seem to mean?

    Ⓐ death

    Ⓑ island

    Ⓒ kingdom

    Ⓓ responsibility

2 What really happens to the dodos in the story?

_____

_____

_____

3 What keeps the dodos from recognizing the real situation?

    Ⓐ their need to help the other animals

    Ⓑ their inability to fly

    Ⓒ the sailors' lies

    Ⓓ their pride

4 How did the absence of predators affect the dodos?

_____

_____

_____

5 Which saying applies to this story?

    Ⓐ Leave no stone unturned.

    Ⓑ Pride goes before the fall.

    Ⓒ A penny saved is a penny earned.

    Ⓓ All things come to those who wait.

Advantage Reading Grade 7 © 2005 Creative Teaching Press

Reading: Comprehension

6 Why do the birds call themselves monarchs?

    Ⓕ The sailors haven't named them dodos yet.

    Ⓖ They think they look like butterflies.

    Ⓗ They want to fly like butterflies.

    Ⓙ They see themselves as rulers.

7 How would this story change if it were told from the rabbits' point of view?

_____

_____

_____

_____

8 What is the likely meaning of *doudo* in the Portuguese language?

    Ⓕ respected

    Ⓖ beautiful

    Ⓗ graceful

    Ⓙ foolish

9 The *dodo* is to *extinct* as the *panda* is to _____ .

    Ⓐ endangered

    Ⓑ beautiful

    Ⓒ graceful

    Ⓓ foolish

10 Why is the setting of this myth so important?

_____

_____

_____

_____

That's Entertainment!

Graphic Information: Time Lines

 This time line traces the development of forms of entertainment that depend on electricity and electronics. After studying the time line, answer the questions on page 102.

Entertainment Time Line

1877	Thomas Edison invents the phonograph
1895	First black-and-white movies shown
1897	Radio signal first sent over long distance
1920	First movies made in color
1930	First jukebox sold in U.S.
1931	First pinball machine sold in U.S.
1941	TV broadcast begins in U.S.
1948	First records sold in U.S.
1954	Color TV first broadcast in U.S.
1957	Stereo phonograph introduced
1962	Video games created
1970	VCRs and CDs first sold
1979	First Sony Walkman sold
1980s	Cable TV networks begin in U.S.
1981	MTV first broadcasts in U.S.

Advantage Reading Grade 7 © 2005 Creative Teaching Press

Reading: **Comprehension**

After studying the timeline on page 102, answer questions 1 through 5.

1 Which form of entertainment did teenagers enjoy first?

    Ⓐ hearing their favorite tunes as they walk to school

    Ⓑ a video recording of their favorite movie

    Ⓒ the latest movie in color at a theater

    Ⓓ their favorite TV sitcom

2 Are you surprised that video games were invented so long ago? Why or why not?

_____

_____

3 Which statement is an opinion?

    Ⓐ Movies were shown in black and white before they were in color.

    Ⓑ It's strange that VCRs and CDs were first sold the same year.

    Ⓒ Video games were invented before cable television.

    Ⓓ MTV is older than you are.

4 Name at least three forms of entertainment that you enjoy and that are missing from this time line. (These kinds of entertainment don't have to depend on electricity or electronics.)

_____

_____

5 *Playing a pinball machine* is to *enjoying a video game* as *writing a letter on stationery* is to _____.

    Ⓐ watching MTV

    Ⓑ playing a DVD

    Ⓒ listening to a CD

    Ⓓ using word processing software

Name _____

That's Entertainment!

Writing: **Narrative**

Narrative writing tells a story, which might be fiction or nonfiction. The purpose is to entertain, and the form might be a personal story, poem, play, eyewitness account, biography, fable, or myth. In a narrative, something happens; usually the main character solves a problem.

To write a narrative, first you must choose a type of narrative and the main idea. To follow the theme of this section, make sure your narrative is entertaining. For example, if you are going to write a personal story, you might focus on a time when everything seemed to go wrong, but it all turned out for the best. Or you might write a fictional story about someone your age who suddenly faces an overwhelming, unexpected change. Or you could write about someone who disagrees with a decision and decides to do something about it. The possibilities, as they say, are endless. The graphic organizer below can help with your planning.

Characters
Setting
Problem/Challenge/Complication
Attempts to Solve It
Final Resolution or Climax
Conclusion

Advantage Reading Grade 7 © 2005 Creative Teaching Press

Name _____

That's Entertainment!

Writing: Narrative

⭐ Now write the first draft of your narrative, using additional paper, if needed. Follow your organizer on page 104. If you are writing a story, you can indicate the personality and values of your characters by what they say, what they do, and how other people react to them. Be sure to include lots of dialogue and try to build suspense as the characters try vainly to solve the problem they face and finally hit upon an approach that works. Don't forget to think of an interesting title for your narrative.

_____

_____

_____

_____

_____

_____

_____

_____

_____

_____

_____

_____

After you finish your first draft, look for ways to make it clearer, more interesting, and better organized. Ask a friend or family member to read it and suggest improvements. For example, does each character's actions make sense? Would that character do that?

Name _____

**That's
Entertainment!**

Writing: **Narrative**

⭐ Now write the final draft of your narrative, using additional sheets of paper, if necessary. Consider your friend or family member's editing suggestions and avoid errors in spelling, punctuation, grammar, and word usage. Illustrate your narrative with one or more drawings.

_____

_____

_____

_____

_____

_____

_____

_____

_____

_____

_____

_____

_____

_____

_____

          Advantage Reading Grade 7 © 2005 Creative Teaching Press

More Things to Do

Try Your Hand

Write a poem, short story, or short message, modeling it after "A Misspelled Tail." Include many homophones (words that sound the same but have different spellings and different meanings). Then challenge a friend to read your work aloud the first time without stumbling on the words.

Start a Book Club

Get together with friends from school or your neighborhood and start an informal book club. You might take turns choosing a book to read (maybe the latest Harry Potter novel) and then discuss what you liked and disliked about it. Or work with your teacher, the school media specialist, or staff at your community library to find out whether a published author lives in your community and might visit your class and share his or her experiences.

Find out More about Dodos

Do you wonder how much of *The Dodo's Demise* is true? Why are these birds extinct, really? Check an encyclopedia or the Internet to find out. Excellent sites include *http://news. nationalgeographic.com*. Look for an article titled "Extinct Dodo Related to Pigeons, DNA Shows." You might also research what happened to other extinct species, such as the passenger pigeon, which once flew over the United States in flocks so large that they blocked out the sun.

Check out these books.

Early Pleasures & Pastimes by Bobbie Kalman (Crabtree)
The History of Moviemaking: Animation and Live-Action, From Silent to Sound, Black-and-White to Color (Scholastic)
Home Entertainment by Rodney Dale and Rebecca Weaver (Oxford University Press)
What Was It Like Before Television? by Rosie Hankin (Steck-Vaughn)

Page 5

Students' word webs might include words such as *habitat, food, endangered species, terrorism, conservation,* and others.

Page 6

1 C
2 G
3 D
4 G
5 B
6 J

Page 7

1 because
2 Next or Then
3 Also or In addition
4 However, But, or Nevertheless
5 For example
6 First
7 However or Nevertheless
8 Also or In addition

Page 9

1 B
2 Possible answers: They do not refer to a previous earthquake; they did not recognize the rumble as the start of an earthquake.
3 A
4 Possible answers: They live in an area that tends to have earthquakes, and people expect them and build houses to withstand them. There was a major quake there in 1971 that people probably talked about.
5 C

Page 10

1 C
2 F
3 D
4 F
5 C
6 G

Page 11

1 except
2. desert
3 farther
4 implied
5 elusive
6 adept
7 morality
8 accept
9 infer
10 adapt
11 dessert
12 adopt
13 mortality
14 further
15 illusive

Page 12

1 B
2 H
3 D
4 F
5 D
6 H
7 A
8 F

Page 14

1 D
2 G
3 B
4 Possible answers: People wear clothing to suit the weather, or they heat and air-condition their homes and buildings.
5 Possible answers: Both have special features to help them adapt to their environment. Jackrabbits cool off through their huge ears. Kangaroo rats cool off by staying in cool underground dens.

Page 16

1 A
2 F
3 A

4 Possible fact: Some zoos help breed endangered species. Possible opinion: Zoos should not cage animals.
5. Sample answers: Cause: Zoos breed endangered animals. Effect: This safe habitat allows the species to reproduce, protecting it from extinction.

Page 18

1 A
2 Possible answer: This fable is based on a natural phenomena and does not have animal characters that behave like people.
3 D
4 Students' new morals should make sense and reflect the real danger of a volcanic eruption or major earthquake. They might warn readers not to underestimate Mother Nature or not to jump to conclusions based on the presence of the mouse, for example.
5 C

Page 20

1 The other Canary Islands would probably end up completely underwater, at least for a short time.
2 F
3 B
4 Possible answers: other coastal areas of West Africa, Great Britain, the entire East Coast of the United States, the islands off the east coast of Canada
5 D

Pages 21–23

Students' fables should be short and clear, with a conflict and outcome that leads logically to their moral. The characters could be animals or people. The conflict might or might not involve a natural phenomena.

Page 25

Students should list information or questions in each section of the chart.

Page 26
1 C
2 H
3 C
4 F
5 C
6 H

Page 27
1 D
2 H
3 C
4 F
5 D
6 H

Page 29
1 C
2 G
3 A
4 H

Page 30
1 D
2 Possible answers: He writes to the citizens of Texas and to all Americans; he stresses liberty, patriotism, and "everything dear to the American character"; he says he will die never forgetting what is due to his country.
3 D
4 Possible answers: his nation's enemy (Mexico, in this case); those who lack patriotism or self-respect; anyone who would surrender or retreat; cowards
5 A

Page 31
1 accent
2 already
3 cease
4 detract
5 deceased
6 ascent
7 elicit
8 later
9 all ready

10 distract
11 seize
12 diseased
13 illicit
14 assent
15 latter

Page 32
1 A
2 H
3 B
4 F
5 B
6 H
7 B
8 J

Page 35–36
1 B
2 Possible answer: About 150 Texas rebels occupied the Alamo when Mexican General Santa Anna attacked with thousands of troops. The Alamo commander, Colonel Travis, appealed for reinforcements, but only 32 men came. After 13 days, the Mexican army stormed the Alamo, killing all the defenders. Still, when others heard about the defenders' courage, they were inspired to fight and win independence for Texas.
3 A
4 H
5 C
6 Possible answer: Texas would have won its independence from Mexico even sooner, perhaps immediately. The courage of the Alamo defenders inspired Texans to defeat Santa Anna on April 21 at San Jacinto, and Texas became a republic in May. If the defenders had been victorious, Texas might have become a republic in March, right after the Battle of the Alamo.
7 C
8 Possible answer: Students' answers should show an understanding of the situation at the Alamo. Most will probably say that the defenders were brave, not foolish. They held out because they hoped to have

reinforcements and because they believed deeply in the cause of freedom. Perhaps they also thought that Santa Anna would kill them even if they surrendered.
9 A

Page 38
1 B
2 G
3 Possible answer: He was discouraged after another election defeat and saw an opportunity to become a leader in a free Texas.
4 J
5 Possible answer: Yes, because that was his goal and he already had experience in politics. He also was famous for skills that people valued on the frontier—shooting, hunting, and telling tall tales.

Page 40
1 B
2 Possible answer: The main part of the drawing is the large plaza in front of the Long Barracks, but the main part of the park is a series of buildings and walkways that are behind the Long Barrack Museum. The park is carefully planned for visitors and probably well kept, but the buildings in the drawing seem to be crumbling.
3 B
4 Possible answer: San Antonio is proud to have the Alamo and wants people to visit and learn about the battle there.
5 A

Pages 41–43
Students' outlines should include two to four main ideas and at least one detail related to each idea. Their final, two-page reports should include a title, an interesting introduction, two to four main ideas in paragraph form and supported with details, and a conclusion that stresses the importance of the topic.

Page 45

Students should respond to each question thoughtfully.

Page 46

1 congregate
2 pugnacious
3 somnambulate
4 confidence
5 kinetic
6 initiative
7 prognosis
8 candid
9 immutable
10 mimeograph

Page 47

1 D
2 G
3 C
4 F
5 C
6 H
7 A

Page 49

1 B
2 J
3 C
4 Possible answers include any statement that is a belief, such as these: The broadcast was imaginative; the listeners should have known better.
5 Possible answers include any statement that can be proved, such as these: The play was broadcast in 1938; Franklin Roosevelt was president then.

Page 50

1 C
2 F
3 D
4 J
5 A
6 H

Page 51

1 depraved
2 disapproved
3 incredible
4 ingenious
5 aural
6 least
7 deprived
8 preceding
9 portended
10 lest
11 oral
12 disproved
13 ingenuous
14 incredulous

Page 52

1 B
2 G
3 A
4 G
5 C
6 H
7 B
8 G

Page 55

1 B
2 Possible answer: The author is probably older as he or she focuses on how hard it is to learn how to use new devices, which is more true for older people than for younger ones.
3 A
4 J
5 Possible summary: Technology has a major effect on our daily lives, but it can be frustrating to learn how to use new devices. Hopefully, failures and crashes will decrease in the future, and simple devices will not be made more complex than necessary.

Pages 58–59

1 C
2 Possible answer: Michael isn't sure that living on the Space Oasis is a good idea because he questions whether there is enough room for everyone. When Zack says they have plenty of water, Michael reminds him of how much fun it is to jump in puddles on Earth. Zachary brags about life on the Space Oasis, but he also misses Earth and speaks longingly of coming back for a visit. Both boys are the same in their close bond with Earth.
3 B
4 Possible answer: It's fiction because there is no Space Oasis or fleet of 50 shuttles right now. Only a few astronauts and cosmonauts at a time live in the International Space Station.
5 D
6 Answers may vary. Some students may think Zack is homesick enough to move back to Earth, while others may think he likes living in space, if only Michael were there, too.
7 B
8 Earth is running out of water.
9 A

Page 61

1 C
2 G
3 Sample answers: The greatest number of online users is in North America; about 11 of every 100 people worldwide use online resources; the number of online users is growing fast even in undeveloped nations. (Several other conclusions are also possible.)
4 Possible answers: The number of users will continue to grow, perhaps at an increasing pace; the less-developed nations will not catch up with the developed nations in that time.
5 D

Pages 62–64

Students' directions should include at least four steps and some substeps. The steps should be listed in chronological order and each begin with an active verb. Their directions should begin with a clear title and informative introduction.

Page 66

Answers will vary but should be thoughtful.

Page 67

1 metastasis
2 hypersensitive
3 benefactor
4 ambivalent
5 magnanimous
6 paraprofessional
7 prototype
8 circumspect

Page 68

1 A
2 H
3 B
4 H
5 A
6 G
7 C
8 H

Page 71

1 B
2 F
3 B
4 H
5 C
6 F
7 D

Page 72

1 fiscal
2 finale
3 message
4 lose
5 pursue
6 voracious
7 access
8 altogether

9 physical
10 finally
11 massage
12 loose
13 all together
14 veracious
15 perused
16 excess

Page 73

1 B
2 G
3 A
4 H
5 A
6 F
7 A
8 F

Page 76

1 B
2 Pushing down on the back of the board causes an equal and opposite reaction as the ground pushes up, sending the skater into the air.
3 B
4 F
5 c, d, b, a

Page 79

1 B
2 Answers may vary. For example, some students may think that Ben will gain enough self-confidence to become a leader, while others may believe that he does not have the outgoing personality of a leader.
3 A
4 Answers may vary. For example, some students may think that Jordan wants to win more and cares more about winning than he cares about others' feelings. Other students may think that Benjamin has won far less often, and so winning would mean more to him.
5 C

Page 81

1 B
2 The bus leaves earlier to get to Kennedy.
3 D
4 G
5 Possible answer: Both teams play at 3:30 and have an equal number of home and away games. The girls play on Tuesdays and Thursdays, while the boys play on Wednesdays and Fridays. The boys will play two games every week, but for some reason the girls have no games one week, so their schedule has six games instead of eight.

Pages 82–84

Students' biographies should be well organized and as complete as possible. They should also make it clear why they chose the subject of their biography.

Page 86

Students should provide eight to ten phrases that relate to entertainment and then compare their webs with a partner, if possible.
1 Answers will vary, but they should be thoughtful.
2 Different people enjoy different types of entertainment.

Page 87

1 C
2 G
3 D
4 F

Page 88

1 D
2 H
3 A
4 G
5 B
6 H

Page 90

1 C
2 F
3 A
4 H

Page 91

1 buoys
2 air
3 fourth
4 nay
5 way
6 weather
7 reins
8 through
9 flew
10 right
11 meets
12 sum
13 knew
14 whole
15 piece
16 rowed

Page 92

1 alter
2 assistance
3 attendants
4 aisles
5 aide
6 bail
7 bearing
8 basis
9 ad
10 billed
11 boarders
12 bullion
13 corral
14 site
15 current
16 counsel

Page 93

1 A
2 F
3 A
4 F
5 A
6 G
7 A
8 F

Page 96

1 Sample answer: She was born in England in 1965 and always loved to write. She didn't like working as a secretary and started writing her first Harry Potter book when she was a teacher. She had trouble finding a publisher, but now her books are enormously successful, as are the movies and products based on them. Rowling is now a billionaire, but she keeps on writing.

2 H
3 D
4 F
5 Students should understand that it is very difficult for an unknown writer to find a publisher, so yes, many unknown writers may be just as talented as Rowling but unable to convince publishers to print their books.

Pages 100–101

1 A
2 The sailors eat the foolish dodos for dinner.
3 D
4 They had no enemies, no animals that wanted to eat them. Thus, they could reproduce in peace and grow in number.
5 B
6 J
7 Sample answer: The rabbits would describe the dodos as foolish, greedy bullies who somehow assumed that only they knew how things should be done. The rabbits might have watched with glee as the sailors picked off the dodos, one by one, until none was left to torment the other animals.

8 J
9 A
10 The story had to begin long ago, before people visited Mauritius. The island had to be isolated to allow the dodos to develop into large birds that could not fly and had no predators.

Page 103

1 C
2 Answers may vary. Some students may have assumed that video games are a new invention because they are currently so popular.
3 B
4 Possible answers: reading books, talking with friends, playing sports, playing cards and other games, playing electronic games, and others
5 D

Pages 104–106

Students' narratives should be clear, organized, and interesting. Their characters should be well developed, and the events should make sense. Ideally the characters will face a problem and try different ways to solve it before reaching success.

Advantage Reading Grade 7 © 2005 Creative Teaching Press